D1610770

A Medical History
of the Colony & Protectorate
of Kenya

A personal memoir

A Medical History
of the Colony and Protectorate
# of Kenya

A personal memoir

JOHN A. CARMAN

Rex Collings • London • 1976

First published by Rex Collings Ltd
69 Marylebone High Street, London W1

© John Carman

SBN 901720 88 7

Typesetting by Malvern Typesetting Services
Printed in Great Britain by
Billing & Sons Limited
Guildford, London and Worcester

PREFACE

In writing this short history of medicine in Kenya, it has been impossible to avoid making a large number of personal references. This is because like most of my contemporary colleagues, some of whom would have been far more competent to write the work, I was myself part of the history I was recording, for I lived through more than thirty years of it.

In writing of past days I have referred to places and institutions by the names which they bore at the time. Many of these names have been changed since Kenya achieved independence and I wish to emphasize the fact that I yield to no one in my respect for the admirable stable government which has been established under President Jomo Kenyatta. Thus I crave the indulgence of my readers for not always using the new names.

It is with the utmost pleasure that I look back upon the years which I spent in Kenya and I remember with sincere affection the many African friends I made there.

J.A.C.,
Salisbury,
England

CHAPTER I

If one stands by Fort Jesus on the water-front of Mombasa, one can watch the incoming dhows brought down from Arabia by the north-east monsoon, as with the strident sound of conch-shell trumpets they sail round the corner to the old harbour adjoining Mombasa Club. Later they may continue their journey further south to Zanzibar or beyond, until with the seasonal change of wind they return, driven by the south-east monsoon to their home ports in Arabia.

For an unknown succession of centuries these small craft have remained virtually unchanged either in their method of construction, their system of navigation or their objective. They carry back with them cargoes of mangrove poles to be used for building purposes in their own treeless land.

It is fascinating to speculate upon the possibility that when Solomon, King of Israel sent his ships, crewed by Sidonian sailors to fetch gold from fabulous Ophir, they followed the same route down the Red Sea, round Cape Guardafui and so southwards along the African coast. It has been suggested that Ophir was the city which once flourished on the site of what are now known as the Zimbabwe ruins. Certainly Solomon did not send his ships to Arabia or Abyssinia, for the account in the Bible clearly states that the return journey took a full year, so that the destination must have been much further south. The ancient port of Sofala which lies in about the same latitude as Zimbabwe, could well have been their objective and if it was, what is more likely than that these old ships should have called at Mombasa to take in fresh water? If they did then the East African Coast had contacts with the Mediterranean nearly three thousand years ago.

Archaeological investigators have shown that traders from China, Malaya and India visited East Africa centuries before any Europeans came on the scene and it was not until 1498 that Vasco da Gama carried the Portuguese flag as far north as Malindi. Portuguese colonies were later founded and for 200 years the Portuguese held sway from Malindi to Sofala.

In about the sixth century AD Arabs from Muscat and Oman began to settle all along the East African littoral and they established strong-points at Kilwa, Malindi and Mombasa. By the fifteenth century their society had built up a high degree of civilization and luxury. They cultivated the fertile coastal plain with slave labour and they became the masters and aristocrats of the land. They lived in solid stone-built houses and worshipped in mosques many of which still stand. An appreciation of their prosperity and standard of living may be gained by a visit to the ruined city of Gedi near Malindi. Not unnaturally they resented the coming of the Portuguese and there were many and bitter struggles between the two races. In 1593 the Portuguese, having gained possession of Mombasa, fortified the town by building Fort Jesus at the entrance to the harbour.

In 1827 Seyid Said, Sultan of Muscat visited his outlying possession of Zanzibar which was ruled by a governor whom he, Seyid Said had appointed. In 1840, becoming tired of the ceaseless internecine warfare which went on in the Hadramaut, Seyid Said moved to take up permanent residence in Zanzibar.

In May 1944 Dr Krapf, a German missionary of the London Missionary Society arrived in Mombasa. He had wanted to work in Abyssinia, but finding that this was impossible, he decided to remain in East Africa and at Rabai some seven or eight miles inland from Mombasa, he set up his station. The early days of his ministry were overshadowed by tragedy. In July he went down with malaria and while he was still ill his wife who was pregnant was also attacked on 5 July. She died on the 15th only five days after the birth of her baby which quickly followed her to the grave. A sad and very inauspicious beginning to what was to be a long and distinguished career.

Krapf was later joined by Rebmann, a fellow-countryman who was the first white man to see the snow-capped peak of Mount Kilimanjaro. While travelling in the Chagga country he was looking towards the mountains in the south-east and, ' . . . at about 10-o-clock I fancied I saw the summit of one of them covered with a dazzling white cloud.' He was astonished by this sight and on enquiring from his African guide he learned that the white substance on the mountain-top was called by the local people 'baridi', which he knew to be the Swahili word for 'cold'. Krapf in his turn saw the white peak on 10 November 1849 and wrote in his diary, 'This morning we had a beautiful view of the snow-mountain Kilimanjaro . . . I could discern that its white crown must be snow.' When this sensational discovery was later communicated to the Royal Geographical Society in London, the learned armchair pundits ridiculed the idea that snow could exist on or near the equator, however high the mountain.

In 1849 Krapf penetrated far into the interior, reaching Kitui in Ukambani and while he was there he was shown another snow-capped mountain, thus becoming the first white man to see Mount Kenya, with its twin peaks and glistening glaciers.

Seyid Said died in 1856 and was succeeded by Seyid Majid. At that time there had been a British Consul in Zanzibar for some 70 years and in 1865 on the retirement of Colonel Playfair from the appointment, Dr G. E. Seward took over while Dr John Kirk became Agency Surgeon. Kirk was peculiarly suited to his new tasks having accompanied David Livingstone on several of his journeys into the interior and his medical duties in Zanzibar were both varied and valuable, though he also filled certain political functions. Thus there began a career which was to have a profound influence on the whole future of East Africa. Kirk became Vice-Consul in 1867 and Consul-General in 1870. In that same year Seyid Majid died and in his successor, Sultan Barghash, Kirk recognized a man of greatly superior intelligence and integrity. The keynote of British policy at this time was the endeavour to stamp out the iniquitous slave-trade between African and Asiatic ports and it was Kirk's diplomacy which eventually secured the co-operation of Barghash, much against the Sultan's personal material interests. It was Kirk's wish to ensure that the suzerainty of the Sultan of Zanzibar over the coastal strip of the mainland should be secured by the establishment of a British Protectorate, but this was not as yet to be.

It is unquestionably true to say that at that time Great Britain had no colonial ambitions in East Africa, but two Germans, Peters and Juhlke had very different ideas. They opened negotiations with a number of Chiefs in what later became Tanganyika Territory and secured concessions over which Kaiser Wilhelm I proclaimed German suzerainty and gave his imperial blessing to the newly formed German East African Company which had the frank objective of extensive colonization. By a similar dubious process another German named Dernhardt gained control of the district around Witu near Lamu.

Sultan Barghash protested vigourously against these infringements of his sovereign rights and wrote a letter to the German Emperor setting out his claims. The only result of this was that in 1866 Bismarck openly challenged the Sultan by sending a naval squadron to Zanzibar to coerce him. Kirk, who saw his hopes of setting up a British 'Sphere of influence' vanishing, was put under pressure by the government in England to reason with Barghash who finally yielded under duress to the German demands.

However in 1888 the British East African Company was incorporated and granted a charter; the spheres of influence of the two great powers were then delineated. In 1893 the German East African Company was taken over by the Imperial Government. The same thing happened to the British East African Company, the finances of which were in a parlous state. It too came under the control of the home government and the Protectorate of East Africa came into being under the auspices of the Foreign Office. It was termed a Protectorate because unlike the Germans, the British recognized the sovereign rights of Zanzibar over the coastal strip. In 1895 Sir Arthur Hardinge was HM Consul-General in Zanzibar and in 1896 he was appointed HM Commissioner to the East African Protectorate. At this time the boundary between the German and British territories ran pretty much where it runs to-day, but the Germans still maintained their hold on the Witu area. The boundary between what was to become known as Kenya and Uganda was much further to the east than it now is; approximately where Naivasha stands. Throughout the whole period of the British Administration in East Africa, the Government of Kenya paid an annual sum to the Sultan of Zanzibar as rent for the coastal region and the Sultan's red flag was always flown over Fort Jesus.

Meanwhile Captain, later Lord Lugard had been sent to Uganda where a treaty signed with the Kabaka Mwanga made that country also a British Protectorate. Lugard succeeded in persuading the British Government that the best way of suppressing the slave-trade was to open up the country by building a railway from Mombasa to Lake Victoria. A survey was carried out and construction began in 1896, largely with the the help of coolie labour imported from India. In 1899 the line reached the point where Nairobi now stands and there ensued a period during which progress was held up while plans for the construction of the next section of the track were discussed. It

4

is interesting to reflect that if this delay had occurred only a little later on when the railway had advanced another fifteen or twenty miles, the capital of the Colony would have been sited in the much more salubrious surroundings of Kikuyu or Limuru.

However, while the engineers and surveyors were deliberating, an extensive shanty town with a large Indian bazaar sprang up, a railway workshop was established, and Nairobi was born. Work was eventually restarted and the first train steamed into the terminus at Lake Victoria on 20 December 1901.

The first doctor appointed to the Chartered Company was Dr A. Mackinnon who arrived in 1888 to be joined in the following year by Dr I.S. Macpherson.

It is recorded that in 1891 a Dr T.M. Rae was stationed at Malindi and Lamu. He died in 1893. Another arrival in 1891 was Dr R.A. Moffat who was sent out to work at Kibwezi as a medical missionary, but subsequently joined the staff of the Company. This gentleman had family connections with the great missionary-explorer David Livingstone whose father-in-law was Moffat's grandfather. At this time the Company had no single doctor working between Mombasa and Lake Victoria.

The first Principal Medical Officer to the East African Protectorate was Dr Macdonald with Dr B.L. Hinde and Dr Mann under him. Doctors Mackinnon and Macpherson both went to Uganda where they became the first Medical Officers to the Protectorate which was established in 1894. They were later joined by Dr Moffat.

In 1896 Dr H.A. Boedeker, a doughty newcomer arrived as did also Dr Edwards who was the first medical missionary to work in Mombasa. A Church of Scotland Mission station was opened at Fort Smith (near the site of the modern Kabete) under Dr Baxter and three other medical missionaries named Charters, Moffat and Wilson were sent out by the same Society.

In 1896 Captain James Will, IMS was appointed Medical Officer in charge of the railway construction and he was joined by Lieutenant King and six Medical Officers.

In 1898 and 1899 there was a severe smallpox epidemic in Mombasa.

Another epidemic, this time of bubonic plague broke out in Nairobi. The various doctors who were brought in to cope with the situation were unanimously of the opinion that the best way to halt the spread of infection was to burn down the rat-infested hovels in the Indian bazaar and several of them proceeded to do so. Dr Spurier was sent from Zanzibar to take overall charge of the medical measures and he put a stop to the sporadic burnings. Nevertheless those who had adopted this somewhat extreme means of control were officially thanked by the Secretary of State in England.

In 1902 the territory east of Lake Victoria was transferred from Uganda to Kenya.

Dr Moffat was transferred from Uganda to be Principal Medical Officer of Kenya and established his headquarters in Nairobi. Dr P. H. Ross was appointed Bacteriologist. In 1906 Dr, formerly Captain, James Will became PMO. The seat of Government was shifted from Mombasa to Nairobi in 1907.

In 1909 the records show that the only hospital in a Native Reserve was that at Fort Hall and in 1910 the personnel of the Medical Department consisted of:

> The PMO and 3 SMOs
> 15 Medical Officers.
> 1 Medical Officer of Health.
> 1 Bacteriologist.
> 4 Assistant Surgeons.
> 18 Sub-Assistant Surgeons.
> 22 Compounders. (Dispensers)
> The Matron of the Nairobi
>   European Hospital.
> 6 Nursing Sisters.
> The Matron of Mombasa gaol
>   and female European Mental
>   Hospital.

The mental hospital in Nairobi was opened in 1910 at Mathari with accommodation for two Europeans and eight Africans. Nairobi European Hospital was opened in 1912.

In 1920 the Kenya Branch of the British Medical association was founded and the Public Health Ordinance was formulated in the same year.

Government medical work was started in Kakamega in 1920 by Dr

1. *Staff Old African Hospital Nairobi 1934*

2. *Rural Dispensaries*
   (a) Old
   (b) New

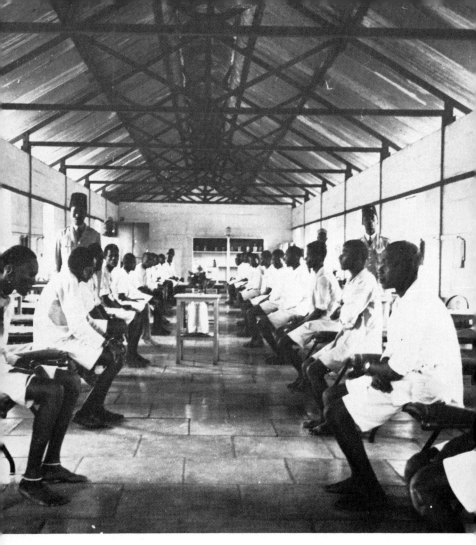

3. *Ward interior old Infectious Diseases Hospital, Nairobi*

4. *Locally made Anaesthetic Apparatus, see page 105*

5. *Brigadier Ogilvie operating with locally trained Anaesthetist 1944*

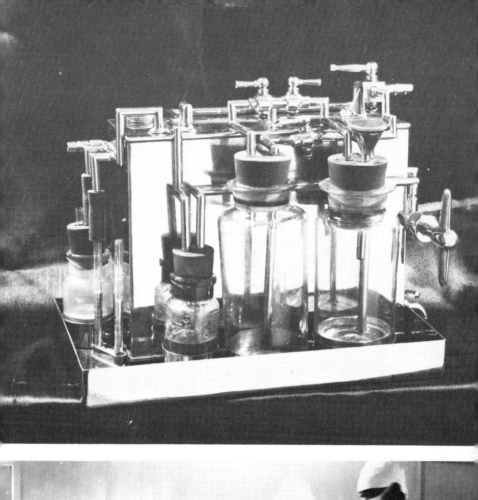

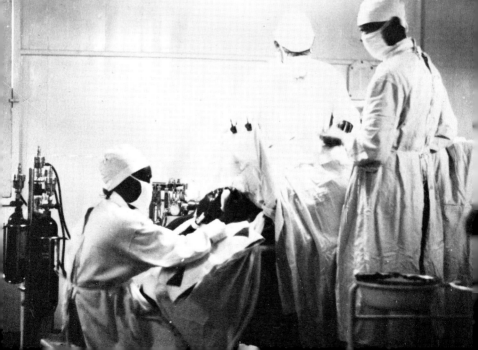

6. *(a) Old Hospital, Nairobi 1926*
(b) Its replacement 1946

P. Nunan. There was no hospital, but a chain of dispensaries was established. In 1920 hospitals were built at Kisii and Machakos, that for Kakamega was opened in 1928.

In 1926 the headquarters of the Medical Department was moved up to a site in Bishop's Road near the Secretariat and the old building near the railway station was used as a medical store.

The following is is a list in chronological order of the arrivals of the early medical men:

1888 A. D. Mackinnon.
1889 I. S. Macpherson.
1891 R. A. Moffat; T. M. Rae.
1895 S. L. Hinde; N. M. Leys.
1896 H. A. Boedeker; Baxter; Charters; Moffat and Wilson.
     Captain Turner, IMS; Lieutenant King and 6 MOS.
1901 C. A. Wiggins; C. L. Chevalier.
1902 E. J. Wynstone-Waters.
1903 P. H. Ross.
1904 W. O. Pritchard; H. L. Henderson; James Will.
1905 V. A. L. Van Someren.

The original headquarters of the government of East Africa was at Mombasa and in 1903 the Governor, Sir Charles Eliott, recognizing the potentialities of the hinterland, wrote in a report that the unoccupied lands in the highlands of East Africa were eminently suited for colonization by Europeans. From that time onwards settlers began to arrive in ever-increasing numbers; many Boers, dissatisfied with conditions in South Africa, trekked up in their ox-wagons and made their homes in the future Kenya, notably in what was known as the Uasin Gishu country. So the stage was set for the opening up of the country when progress was abruptly halted by the outbreak of the 1914 - 1918 war.

CHAPTER II

In the early phases of the history of the Colony, the sole object which the authorities had in mind when providing medical services was to cater for the needs of the officials and their families. English doctors were stationed in the main administrative centres, but there were Goan doctors and Indian sub-assistant surgeons to care largely for the Indians engaged on the railway construction. With the advent of settlers the picture began to change and a number of settler-doctors came into being. One such was Dr H. L. Henderson who practised for many years in Nakuru.

With the outbreak of war in 1914 there was the possibility of a German invasion across the frontier between the British and German colonies. There can be no doubt that the German settlers were much better organized than the British, who in fact were not organized at all. They were, however both anxious and willing to defend their homes and there was an immediate rush, almost a stampede of settlers from all parts of the Colony to Nairobi, demanding to be put into uniform and sent to fight the emeny. The Government had made no preparations for dealing with so many belligerent gentlemen and there was a good deal of embarrassment. However, things were eventually sorted out and among the units which were formed was the East African Mounted Rifles. The Medical Officer to this regiment was Dr C. J. Wilson who was in the EA Medical Service and was universally known as 'Dan' Wilson. He served right through the war and his task was not only adventurous, but also onerous, especially in the terminal stages of the campaign when the British forces had invaded German territory and were hunting Von Lettow-Vorbeck and his elusive men through the bush country. Endemic diseases like malaria, dysentery and enteric fever were much more dangerous and effective enemies than the German General and Dan Wilson has told the story of the regiment and all its vicissitudes in a fascinating history of the East African Mounted Rifles.

When the war came to an end and its aftermath had receded, the Colony entered a phase of rapid expansion, due in part to the influx of soldier settlers anxious to invest their war-gratuities in what they hoped would prove to be a land of promise. It follows that all departments of Government had to be correspondingly increased to provide services for the swelling population. One important problem was the provision of African labour to work on farms and estates and a little thought will show how many administrative difficulties arose in this one field alone.

By 1924 there were in the Medical Department, thirty-three British MOs, seven stationed in Nairobi, three at Mombasa, and one each at Kakamega, Kisii, Fort Hall, Chuka, Nakuru, Narok, North Jubaland and Moyale. Two more were seconded to the Uganda Railway to look after staff engaged on the construction of the new Uasin Gishu branch line. A further eight were on leave for in those days a tour of service in the Colony varied from eighteen to thirty months so that at any given time about one third of all the officials were on leave in England and this was a very sore point with the settler community.

In addition to the full-time MOs there were four part-time District Surgeons, like the Dr Henderson referred to above, all located in settled areas and to supplement its European staff, the Medical Department employed a number of Sub-Assistant-Surgeons who were recruited in India where they had undergone varying types and degrees of training. They did not hold registrable medical qualifications, but the Principal Medical Officer was empowered to grant them licences to practise medicine in the Colony. They were entitled to engage in private practice, but if they left the Colony their licences were invalid. Many of these men were valuable and efficient subordinate officers and in exceptional cases their loyal services were recognized by their being allowed to continue in practice after they retired. In one or two instances notable war-time service was rewarded by promotion to the higher rank of Assistant Surgeon.

Some personal reminiscences will give some indication of the conditions which prevailed in Nairobi when I arrived in Kenya in February 1926. On arrival at Mombasa I was met by Dr R. J. Harley-Mason who later became the Colony's first ophthalmic specialist. He helped me through the customs and entertained myself, my wife and my daughter at his house until in the late afternoon he saw us off in the train for Nairobi. It would have been unthinkable for any newly-appointed official not to be met in this way and again when we arrived at Nairobi we were met.

In 1926 the permanent way was laid on the iron sleepers which were necessary because of the ubiquitous white ants and there was no ballast on the track and seen from outside, the train could be observed to proceed on its way enveloped in a cloud of red dust. This dust penetrated into one's compartment; it found its way into every piece of luggage, covered one's face, hands and clothes and got into one's eyes, ears and nose. There were no corridor coaches but each compartment was fitted with a let-down wash-bowl and a WC annexe. Meals were served en route at specified points. There was only a single line so that the train stopped at every station where the driver had to ensure that the way was clear for him to enter the next section. The engine was fired with wood fuel cut in the adjacent bush and stacked at the side of the track to be picked up as it was required.

All this was very novel to us and to add to our interest we had a magnificent view of Mount Kilimanjaro in the early morning and saw large numbers of game animals placidly grazing alongside.

We reached Nairobi in the late afternoon and were met by three of my future colleagues who took us to the New Stanley Hotel where rooms had been booked. Nairobi received us with what I can only describe as a blaze of glory. While my wife was putting our child to bed I went for a walk and knowing nothing of the way in which the town was laid out, I had turned into the sanitary lane behind Government Road, when chancing to look up, I saw flames in the upper storey of one of the shops. As I watched this somewhat unusual phenomenon the roof of the building fell in and the flames shot skywards. A high wind was blowing and the fire spread rapidly from building to building since nearly all of them were made of wood and corrugated iron. Since the wind was blowing down towards our hotel, I became seriously alarmed lest sparks might be blown to it across the road and I hurried back to find that all the lights had gone out and I had to rescue my wife and child from the bathroom with a candle. The fire reached nearly to the junction of what was then called sixth Avenue (Kenyatta Avenue), and Government Road and then fortunately the wind dropped and all danger was past. The only medical connotation of this event was a remark by the Medical Officer of Health, who said it was a pity that the fire had not been in the Indian Bazaar; perhaps he was looking back to the plague epidemic of 1902.

My finances could not stand the New Stanley prices so on the Monday morning we moved out to the Salisbury residential hotel. The Salisbury had itself suffered from a recent fire which had destroyed a considerable part of it, but the main building was undamaged and the enterprising proprietress whose husband was in in the Public Works Department had borrowed a number of tents and we were housed in one of these. However, the weather was fine and we suffered no real inconvenience.

On the Monday morning I set off to report to my boss at Medical Headquarters and I adopted the only means of transport, to wit a rickshaw. The offices were housed in a building near the railway station and the ground floor was given over to the medical stores. I mounted the stairs, walked along a passage and found myself confronted by an imposing-looking individual whom I thought must be the PMO himself. He was reading a newspaper and for some time took no notice of me, then presently he looked up with an air of condecension and enquired my name and qualifications. These he proceeded to verify in a somewhat battered copy of the Medical Register. He looked at me severely and said,

'I see that you have the MRCS, LRCP, but there is no mention against your name of the MB, BS.' I suggested that I might have obtained my degree after his copy of the Register had been published. At this moment an inner door opened and a tall handsome man appeared.

'Ogden' he said, 'How dare you question Dr Carman's word and in future when you address him, call him "Sir".' He then took me inside and introduced himself as Dr Wilson, Deputy PMO, explaining that Dr Gilks the PMO was on leave. Dan Wilson was one of the most charming men whom it has ever been my good fortune to meet and I remember being impressed by the brightness of his clear blue eyes. He asked me where I was staying and when I told him that we were under canvas he showed genuine concern, promising that he would see that a house should be allotted to me as soon as one became available. We had a long talk during which he impressed upon me that the primary over-riding duty of all MOs was the clinical care of the African people and on the public health level to promote the improvement of their standards of living. He then told me that my first concern must be the purchase of a car and when I replied that I had not thought of indulging in such a luxury he assured me that far from being a luxury, a car was an essential since I could not do my job without one. There was however, a scheme whereby one could obtain a loan to cover the cost of the car and its insurance. The loan was interest-free, repayable over two years and one could draw an allowance of a shilling a mile while travelling on duty.

When I had submitted my original application to the Colonial Office, I had mentioned that during the war I had served in the Territorial Sanitary Company of the RAMC and this had created the wholly erroneous impression that I was more interested in public health than in clinical medicine. Accordingly I was to work at the Health Office under Dr J. C. Carlyle-Johnstone to whom I was told to report forthwith. At that time the town of Nairobi had no MOH of its own. Dr Wilson then wished me good morning and ordered the now obsequious Ogden to drive me to the Health Office in Government Road.

For charm and friendliness, Johnstone came very near to the standard set by Dan Wilson and after we had had a general talk about my future work he gave me some sound advice as to suitable cars and I set out to buy one. I settled for a box-body Rugby, a make which has long since ceased to exist, but mine gave me good service for more than two years,

The medical set-up in Nairobi at this time comprised the PMO, Dr J. Langton Gilks, his Deputy, Dr C. J. Wilson and two senior medical officers, one of whom, Dr Albert Rutherford Paterson was solely concerned with public health and the other who possessed the sonorous name of Dr Alfred Donald John Bedward Williams, dealt with medical matters and general administration. Then there was the Medical Research Laboratory under Dr W. H. Kauntze who later became DMS in Uganda and his assistant Dr G. V. Allen who was shortly to be promoted to an appointment in Malaya. Dr Johnstone at the Health Office had two MOs under him as well as a staff of Sanitary Inspectors. The Medical Officer in charge of the European Hospital was always chosen for his ability as a surgeon and he was also responsible for the medical needs of all the officials in Nairobi and their families. The Medical Officer in charge of the Native Hospital also needed to be a competent surgeon and in addition he supervised the large General Dispensary down in the town and Mathari Mental Hospital. The Infectious Diseases Hospital, the Police Depot Dispensary and the Prison Hospital as well as the Approved School at

Kabete were all under the Health Office.

All Government doctors were entitled to engage in private practice, but in Nairobi this did not amount to much except in the case of the man at the European Hospital where he had what virtually amounted to a monopoly since no private doctors were allowed to treat patients there. He did all the surgery and was allowed to charge half fees for operations performed on the wives and families of officials. This 'closed shop' was a sore point with the private practitioners. There was no maternity ward at the hospital and there was a set scale of fees for baby cases one or two of which came my way, but the only other supplementary cash I earned was for the odd anaesthetic and for examining rickshaw boys who had to have a certificate of medical fitness for which one could charge a shilling.

There were six general practioners in Nairobi; G. V. W. Anderson and his assistant T. Farnworth Anderson, (no relation), Dr Burkitt, whose nephew achieved such distinction for his work on the tumour which bears his name, Dr Mackinnon who had some pretension to being a Paediatrician, Major Clarke, a retired officer of the IMS and his wife Dr Violet Clarke. There was one consulting physician, Dr A. J. Jex-Blake, the son of a headmaster of Rugby, who had married Lady Muriel Herbert, daughter of the Earl of Pembroke, Jex-Blake had been on the staff of the Brompton Chest Hospital in London, but was advised for health reasons to live in a warmer climate. He bought a small coffee farm just on the fringe of Nairobi and was a most valuable member of the medical fraternity.

Prior to the war almost the sole function of the Medical Department had been the care of the health of the officials, but now much more attention was being paid to the needs of the general African population and several new hospitals had been opened in the Native Reserves, notably at Kiambu, Keruguya, Wesu in the Teita Hills, Meru and Kakamega. There was also an MO stationed at Maseno in Central Nyanza, but he had no hospital.

The number of Assistant Surgeons available was quite inadequate to cope with the rapid influx of new settlers and a scheme was inaugurated whereby a doctor was granted a free farm in a settled area on the understanding that he would practise medicine in the district. One such man, Dr John Sterry travelled out with us in the same ship. He went to work at Thika where he rendered valuable to the community over many years.

There were also many medical missionaries in the country belonging chiefly to the Church Missionary Society, the Church of Scotland and several Roman Catholic missions. There were mission hospitals at Kikuyu, Maseno, Kaloleni, near Dr Krapf's old station at Rabai, Chogoria and Tumu-Tumu on the slopes of Mount Kenya and there was one Methodist Medical Mission in the Tana River District.

When Sir Patrick Manson began campaigning in London for a hospital and school of tropical medicine, many of his colleagues were highly sceptical and flouted the idea that a speciality existed in this field, but he replied by offering to set an examination paper which none of them would be able to answer. The challenge was not taken up. The London School of Tropical Medicine was opened in 1899 at the Royal Albert Docks, but it was moved to Endsleigh Gardens Bloomsbury in 1921. In 1924 it was amalgamated with the new School of Hygiene under the directorship of Dr (Later Sir) Andrew Balfour. It was obligatory for all recruits to the IMS and the Colonial Medical Service to attend a course of study at this school before taking up their appointments, but in my case because of the urgent need for more doctors in Kenya this regulation was waived until my first home leave. In the event this proved to be an advantage rather than the reverse because during my first tour of service I gained a good deal of practical experience which was very valuable during the course and moreover I was able to gather material for an MD thesis.

A list of the diseases prevalent in Kenya in 1926 would, if arranged in alphabetical order, read rather like the index of a text-book of tropical medicine. Malaria was endemic and often epidemic throughout most of the country and was almost exclusively the malignant tertian form caused by *Plasmodium falciparum*. Attacks were commonly very virulent and in August 1928 Sir Christian Felling, General Manager of the Uganda Railway died of malaria. Blackwater fever claimed many victims and in spite of popular beliefs to the contrary it attacked Africans as well as Europeans, albeit less commonly. When the synthetic antimalarial drugs were introduced blackwater fever virtually disappeared, which lends credence to the view that it was caused by the injudicious use of quinine. Although there had been an extensive vaccination campaign, smallpox was not uncommon, plague was endemic and leprosy was widespread, especially in the coastal belt and around the shores of Lake Victoria. Yaws was so prevalent that it posed a major

14

problem; syphilis and gonorrhoea were common. Intestinal parasites like *Necator americanus* (almost universal at the Coast), *Ascaris lumbricoides* and *Taenia saginata* were all very commonly seen. Onchocerciasis and filariasis were less common and were naturally restricted as to their incidence. Dengue was not often encountered; it was usually associated with a recent immigrant from India and perhaps local conditions were such that it failed to establish itself. Both relapsing fever and tick typhus occurred and typhoid and paratyphoid were common enough. Amoebic dysentery and amoebic abscess of the liver were met with, also the less virulent types of bacillary dysentery. There was a great deal of African malnutrition and one form known as kwashiorkor was particularly common in young children in and around Nairobi. There was a very high level of infant mortality and it was estimated that eighty per cent of all African babies born died before they were a year old. During my first tour of service I saw plenty of cases of anthrax and several of tetanus, but the great killer was pneumonia which often supervened as a terminal event in malaria and other debilitating diseases. Although it had not been recognized at the time kala-azar was endemic in some parts of Kenya.

The commonest surgical condition was the tropical ulcer and every newly-appointed MO was alleged to discover some new and better way of treating it. Traumatic injuries were common enough as might be expected, but malignant disease was rare in Africans, so rare that it used to be supposed that for some unknown reason they enjoyed a selective racial immunity. Such is not, however, the case. In former years few Africans lived to the cancer age, but now that they enjoy a much longer life-expectancy, cancer is often diagnosed. In women who had undergone the rite of female circumcision the resultant scarring was such as often to necessitate Caesarian section when they came into labour. Another very common gynaecological disease was pelvic peritonitis due to gonococcal infection. Patients, particularly women, with enlarged thyroids would seek operation for purely cosmetic reasons, but in general Africans did not bother much about tumours unless they were painful.

It was generally taken for granted that most Africans suffered from some form or other of dietary deficiency and lack of calcium was thought to be widespread. In the late 1920s a commission was sent out under the auspices of Sir John Boyd Orr to investigate this problem. Its findings were, I believe inconclusive, but attention was

15

drawn to the poor nutritional value of maize meal. Maize meal or 'posho' as it was called, had long been issued as the basic food ration to labourers on estates, porters on safari and in some cases to domestic servants. On safari this did not matter very much because the sportsmen or leaders of the caravan shot plenty of game and the porters got their share. Similarly most housewives supplemented the posho with meat, bread, sugar and tea, but on big estates which employed hundreds of labourers, such dietetic additions as were issued tended to be grossly inadequate. This state of things was held to account for the high incidence of tropical ulcer as well as the almost universally low work-output in terms of man-hours. Maize is well known to be deficient in at least one of the essential vitamins and should never have been allowed to become a basic article of diet. In the Reserves the people could and did supplement it with herbs gathered to act as relish and they also depended upon other grains such as matama and mwimbi and they drank fair quantities of home-brewed beer which was so thick as almost to constitute a meal in itself. None of these accessories were available when the men were working hundreds of miles from home and they suffered accordingly. Their masters, activated by materialistic considerations issued posho which was the cheapest food available. Whether it was because of recommendations made by Sir John Boyd Orr's Commission or not I am unable to say, but it was made compulsory to add a fixed percentage of wheat flour to all maize meal sold for human consumption.

It will be apparent from what has been said that the patients at the main hospitals presented a very wide variety of conditions, though as yet western medicine had not become very popular and there were many empty beds in the wards. One aftermath of the war was that the hospitals were run on quasi-military lines. For many years these institutions were referred to as 'Native Civil Hospitals', a designation which in the absence of any military hospitals was clearly obsolete. The large war-time military hospital which had been put up in the N'gong Road had been condemned as unfit for further use by the Army, but it was taken over by the Medical Department, renamed the Native Civil Hospital Nairobi, though for years the Africans continued to refer to it as the 'KAR' hospital. It continued to function until after the first two years following the second world war, in spite of having been condemned in 1918.

It was built on the pavilion principle with wards constructed of

16

wood and corrugated iron, with no mosquito-proofing and no running water. The bucket latrines were innocent of the least attempt at fly-proofing. The operating theatre was a small shack with a sterilizing room and an annexe for inducing anaesthesia. The floor was covered with linoleum to prevent dust blowing up through the cracks between the boards, but since the linoleum was soon worn into holes it did little to keep the dust out. The theatre did boast its own water supply, but it is a tribute to the resistance of the African organism to pathogenic bacteria, that there was not more post-operative sepsis.

The hospital was staffed by a Medical Officer in charge who was usually an SMO and who did most of the surgery, two or three junior MOs, an English Matron and Ward Sisters, African dressers who were all males, labourers and sweepers. The word 'sweeper' was borrowed from India and was applied to men who attended to the latrines and handled bed-pans and urine bottles which no one else would touch.

First thing every morning the entire African staff was paraded and inspected by the MO on duty, just as if they had been a company of soldiers. The MO in charge held a formal orderly room at 9.0 a.m. Working hours were from 8.30 a.m. till 4.30 p.m. and these times were strictly adhered to. Any MO who came late or left early was liable to be severely reprimanded and even in my third tour when I had been qualified for ten years I had to ask permission if I needed to go to the bank or get my hair cut. The martinet who was in charge at the time seemed oblivious to the fact that one would have too much sense of responsibility to leave the hospital if there was work left undone. Many and many a time I sat in my little office doing nothing but kill time until the magic hour of 4.30 came round and I could go home.

As was mentioned above there were many empty beds particularly in the surgical wards, for the Africans still had a deeply-rooted fear of anything in the way of operative treatment. There was however, another factor. Dr Gilks the PMO had a queer facet to his character which led him to believe that it was undesirable for anyone, except of course the headquarters staff, to settle down comfortably in one place for any length of time, particularly if his station afforded such amenities as those to be enjoyed in Nairobi. He therefore continually moved men around so that the Africans never knew a doctor long enough for him to establish that vital relationship which can only be built up and lead to real trust and confidence over a period of time. As will be seen later Gilks's more far-seeing successor put this right very soon after he took over the Department.

A battalion of the KAR was always stationed in Nairobi and their barracks and headquarters adjoined the hospital compound. This had one disadvantage because when the regimental band was practising it was almost impossible properly to examine a patient's chest. One ward, the only one built in permanent materials, was reserved for KAR patients and this was under the personal supervision of the Matron, a redoubtable lady named Miss Kenny. All the beds were furnished with red blankets and they were so neatly arranged that they formed a straight line from one end of the ward to the other whenever Miss Kenny made her daily inspection. Every morning at 11 o'clock Miss Kenny presided over the ceremony of morning tea and all members of the European staff were expected to be present; not even the SMO would have ventured to absent himself. Miss Kenny was a force to be reckoned with; she was an intimate friend of Mrs Gilks and any young MO who incurred the Matron's displeasure was liable to find himself on transfer at short notice to one of the less desirable up-country stations.

The European Hospital was situated on Hospital Hill just below the gates of Government House. Here too there was a bucket-latrine system and the only water supply was from a stand-pipe in the compound.

The third hospital which only catered for cases of infectious disease was sited on the fringe of the municipal area beyond the prison. This too was built on the pavilion system with wards constructed of wood and iron, though there was a stone bungalow for European patients. The Superintendent of the hospital was a man called W. J. Henfrey, an ex-NCO of the Indian Army. Bill Henfrey was unquestionably one of the most efficient subordinates in the Department. He was an excellent administrator, an iron dis-ciplinarian and he had such a flair for handling staff that in spite of his strictness they respected him and indeed came very near to loving him as well. Bill was an expert at dark-ground microscopic examination and he was confident that he could distinguish between the spirochaetes of yaws and syphilis, something which the text-books tell us is well-nigh impossible. Of course Bill had exceptional opportunities for examining smears from both diseases and maybe had a good deal more practice than most observers. At all events I

18

never knew him to be at fault.

Apart from Mathari Mental Hospital, the only other medical institution in the capital was the Nairobi Nursing Home. This was in a turning off the Kabete Road just beyond Ainsworth Bridge and it consisted of a small group of bungalows and a separate operating theatre to which patients had to be carried over an open drain on stretchers. It was staffed by a Matron who was also the owner and two or three nursing sisters. It was the only place where the private practitioners could perform surgical operations, but it did not enjoy a very good reputation.

Since there was no maternity hospital and baby cases were not admitted to the European Hospital, confinements had to be domiciliary and there were several freelance private nurses who were available for such cases.

The original shanty town of Nairobi which had arisen when the railway people were deliberating how to get their trains down into the rift valley, was fast disappearing. Whether it was because the insulation on the electric wiring was tending all at once to wear out, I cannot say, but the fact is that there were many fires, some, like that which greeted us on the night of our arrival, very extensive and the tendency was to rebuild in permanent materials. It is difficult to remember when the roadside drains were covered in, but my recollection is that the only street which had a tar-macadam surface was Government Road and I can recall seeing a team of oxen pulling a car out of the mud in Sixth Avenue during the rainy season. Because of the universal bucket-latrine system it was necessary to provide means of access to the backs of all premises by the so-called 'sanitary lanes'. Every night ox-drawn carts popularly spoken of as 'thunder-wagons' went the rounds of all the houses and shops emptying the buckets. These carts were hauled by bullocks of the Ankole breed from Uganda and these animals have the most enormous horns, anything up to six feet or more in length. They were the pride and joy of their drivers who did not have much else to boast about!

There was a very sharp political division in the European community between officials and non-officials. This was because the non-officials thought that the officials were too well paid and that in addition they had many hidden emoluments such as home leave, free furnished quarters and free medical attention. The leader of the unofficials was Lord Delamere the pioneer peer who had done so

19

much to foster stock farming and spent a fortune in the process. There was constant vociferous protest against Government extravagance and the correspondence columns of the newspaper were full of letters on the same subject. The fact that the banks, insurance companies and other large commercial concerns adopted the same policy towards their employees, did not seem to occur to the dissidents, nor did they take account of the fact that people whose homes were in England and had no intention of becoming permanent residents in Kenya, would not enter the service of a colonial dependency which did not provide the facilities to which objection was taken. The settlers were just as antipathetic towards the Indians, but this was more a matter of sour grapes because the Indians being excellent businessmen grew very wealthy and owned a great deal of real estate in the town and for their part clamoured for more adequate representation on Legislative Council. However, since the Colony still depended on substantial grants from the home Government, the gentleman at the Treasury had the whip-hand and there was very little they could do about it especially with a Government majority in Legislative Council.

African servants were universally employed except for a few wealthy people who had Goanese cooks or perhaps Seychelles nannies.

Petty crime was common enough, but serious offences were seldom committed. It was perfectly safe for men and women to walk abroad after dark without fear of molestation and one did not even bother to lock up the house when retiring to bed for the night. There was no racial discrimination like that which exists in South Africa. One rubbed shoulders in the post office or in the shops with African men and women and it was not till after the next war that inter-racial hatred, enmity and loss of respect for the law became the rule instead of the exception.

Because of the shocking state of the country roads which were little more than mere tracks cleared through the bush and became veritable quagmires during the rains, American cars with their more powerful engines and higher clearance were in almost universal use. In Nairobi numbers of people still maintained private rickshaws.

CHAPTER III

The jurisdiction of Nairobi's MOH extended well beyond the confines of the municipality and there was a country hotel some miles out which enjoyed an unusual amenity; it had a swimming pool fed from above by a small stream. One of the first tasks which was assigned to me was to go out and investigate the pool and stream in case there was any danger that people bathing there might contract schistosomiasis. This disease is interesting because it illustrates how many tropical diseases are disseminated through intermediate hosts. The schistosome is a parasitic worm which in some mysterious way has adapted itself to living in the pelvic veins of man. The female worm produces enormous numbers of eggs all of which are furnished with spines and by means of these they work their way either into the bladder or the rectum, whence they are voided in the urine or faeces. If one of these eggs finds its way into water the shell ruptures and a rounded organism called a miracidium escapes to swim freely in search of a water-snail. Any snail will not do, it must be one belonging to the genuses *Bullinus* or *Omphilaria* and having found one of these the miracidium attaches itself to snail's skin and penetrates its body to reach the liver. Here it undergoes development the result of which is the production of vast numbers of embryos called cercariae which are for all the world like minute tadpoles except that they have forked tails. All snails have cercariae in their livers, but only those with bifid tails belong to the genus *Schistosoma*. The cercariae are shed into the water where they can survive for quite long periods and they swim around until they meet a human being whose skin they penetrate and then develop into the adult worm and begin the cycle over again. My job was to collect as many as I could of the right kind of snail and examine them. I found plenty of *Bullinus* and *Omphilaria* in the swimming pool and they all had many cercariae in their livers. However, since none of these had bifid tails I was able to reassure Dr Johnstone and give the hotel swimming pool a clean bill of health.

About this time Lady Grigg the Governor's wife began to interest herself in child welfare and she staged a fête at Government House to raise funds for the establishment of Child Welfare Clinics. Most Departments participated by staging exhibits and ours was no exception. I was detailed to make a model to illustrate the ideal lay-out for a small coffee farm. Being ignorant of the virtues of papier maché, I made the model in plaster of Paris and coloured it with water-colour paint. It looked quite well though its making created an unholy mess. The fête was an unqualified success and before long four clinics were opened for African children, three in the African locations and one in the railway African quarters. I was put in charge of all four and soon after they were established, Lady Grigg expressed a wish to visit them. She was escorted by Dr Paterson and it was my duty as MO i/c to receive her at each, which I did by driving from one to the next as fast as I could down side streets. The Clinic at the Railway Landhies was the first to be visited and I was presented to Lady Grigg when she arrived there. After showing her round I dashed off to the second in Pumwani and when she came in I bowed, but she looked inquiringly at Dr Paterson who introduced me for the second time. The same thing happened at the other two clinics, so in less than an hour the 'Great Lady' had forgotten the humble doctor no less than three times.

For years prior to the opening of these special clinics the African locations had been served by general medical dispensaries which being under the aegis of the Health Office had been placed under my supervision. They were really run by a Health Sister named Rebecca Sharp who was universally known as 'Becky', though I never ventured to call her anything but Miss Sharp to her face. Becky went her rounds on a small two-stroke motor cycle to which the Africans gave the onomotopoeic name of 'pic-a-pic'.

One of the chief functions of these dispensaries was the control and treatment of venereal disease and I devoted one afternoon a week to the diagnosis and therapy of these conditions. There were several African brothels in the town, but the police turned a blind eye on them on the understanding that the women were under regular medical supervision. This was carried out by Becky Sharp with my help. One 'Madame' who ran a thriving institution used to bring her young ladies to the clinic in a string of private rickshaws and while they were being examined in an inner room by Becky I used to pass the time by engaging their mistress, a Nubian of ample proportions, in idle conversation. One day I noticed that she was wearing a necklace of metal beads which were of delicate filigree workmanship and I asked her to let me have a closer look at it. When she took it off and gave it to me I nearly dropped it, so great was its weight and I realized at once that it was made of solid gold. It must have been worth hundreds of pounds and when I returned it I remarked upon its beauty and value. The lady then begged me to accept it as a gift to recompense me for the care I was taking of her girls. She said she could easily spare it because she had two more like it at home. I was forced to decline this mark of her gratitude and explained that as a Government official I was forbidden to accept valuable gifts from my patients. Nevertheless I was sorely tempted, for it was a museum piece worth far more than its intrinsic value.

During the recent war and since, the African brothels had been regularly visited by European men and Becky Sharp was struck as I was by the fact that none of the women ever seemed to become pregnant or to give birth to half-caste children. Half-castes are notoriously common both in South Africa and India, but during my 35 years in Kenya I only remember seeing two and one of them was the fruit of a legitimate marriage between an Englishman and an African woman.

Miss Sharp was quite sure that the African women with whom she came into contact, and these were certainly to be numbered in hundreds, had the secret either of a highly efficient method of contraception or of a powerful, safe abortifacient. She made many efforts to penetrate this secret, but all in vain until one of her patients who was a free-lance prostitute fell ill with double pneumonia. Becky nursed her so sedulously that she reached and passed her crisis and one afternoon she told Becky that to show her gratitude she would reveal the secret of the means whereby African women avoided unwanted pregnancies. When Becky went to her hut to see her next day she found her dead in bed with a wet towel tied over her nose and mouth. In her feeble condition this had been enough to kill her, so whoever had overheard the previous day's conversation had made very sure that the jealously-guarded secret should remain un-revealed. Needless to say the murderer, or more probably the murderess was never brought to book.

A very serious clinical and public health problem was posed by the widespread prevalence of yaws which was particularly common amongst the Kikuyu and the tribes who lived on the shores of Lake Victoria. The problem was complicated by the many similarities between yaws and syphilis, a disease which was also widely distributed and differential diagnosis and treatment were both difficult. Many competent authorities held the view that the two diseases were in fact the same, but to those who worked in the field this theory was quite untenable. The type of syphilis met with in East Africa was mild, seldom giving rise to tertiary manifestations like gummata and central nervous complications. Owing to the close biological similarity between the causal organisms of the two diseases, the two serological tests employed in diagnosis, the Wasserman reaction and the Kahn test were equally positive in both conditions. There was, however one important distinguishing feature; a single dose of 0.6 gm of NAB (Novarseno-billon) would clear up a case of florid yaws and render the serological tests negative, but this did not hold for syphilis, however mild the case might be. As I mentioned earlier, Henfrey at the IDH could and did distinguish between the spirochaetes of the two diseases and conclusive proof came my way when I saw a case of secondary yaws with a primary penile syphilitic chancre co-existing.

Though there was this easy way of treating yaws it was not practical because of the expense. NAB is costly and there were tens of thousands of cases of yaws. It was decided to seek for a less expensive drug. A clinical trial was mounted at the IDH where there were always plenty of yaws patients and the virtues of sodium-potassium-bismuth tartrate were first tested. This involved close co-operation between the MO i/c IDH and the Medical Research Laboratory where the serological tests were carried out. The man at the IDH did not give this essential co-operation and fell out with Dr Kauntze at the laboratory. He was summarily banished to the distant station at Moyale on the northern frontier and I replaced him.

All patients had a Kahn test done and the results were recorded as +, ++, +++, or ++++. Blood tests were performed twice weekly. The double salt of bismuth was effective, but to bring a Kahn test in a case of yaws down from ++++ to negative required a course of three months of regular weekly injections. For a mass field campaign this would have been quite useless. No patient, once his overt symptoms had cleared would come week after week for an injection and he would therefore remain a potential source of infection.

The chemists at the laboratory then perfected a new bismuth preparation. This was a very finely-divided metallic suspension with a dilute carbolic acid base which could be injected through a medium-bore intramuscular needle. The metallic bismuth formed a depôt in the tissues from which it was absorbed slowly over a period of weeks. The advantages of this should be obvious: even if a patient failed to be punctual in his attendances, he still went on treating himself and of course many less injections were needed. The clinical trial at the IDH showed that three injections of metallic bismuth at monthly intervals would render the Kahn test negative in the vast majority of cases, so the suspension was prepared in bulk and distributed to the centres where it was needed. By the time when I left Kenya in 1960 yaws had become so uncommon that most of the recently-joined MOs had never seen a case.

Since the Prison lay on the way from the Health Office to the IDH, it was convenient for the same MO to be in charge of both institutions. This provided valuable experiences because the convicts in the gaol came from all over the Colony and were drawn from many different tribes who were subject to a wide variety of diseases. It was here that I learned a little about the tribal customs of the Masai. A group of young warriors, called in the Masai tongue, 'El moran' had been involved in a ritual murder and sentenced to long terms of imprisonment. The traditional diet of Masai young men is a mixture of blood and milk. The prison diet was posho, boiled beans and whole maize and a bi-weekly ration of meat. This the Masai could not stomach, though they tried their best as they became increasingly hungry. It very soon became apparent that these men would die of starvation unless something was done, so I put in a report to the PMO and after administrative discussions at high level it was agreed to impose a severe fine of cattle instead of the prison sentence and the men were released. It was at Nairobi gaol that I first encountered cases of scurvy and fresh limes were added to the prisoners' rations.

Capital punishment was still in force and it was the distasteful duty of the prison doctor to attend all executions. This was a harrowing business, but someone who was not in the Prison Service had to certify that the hanging had been efficiently and expeditiously carried out and the person concerned had to be a medical man so that he could sign the death certificate. Over the years I witnessed a total of 43 executions.

Corporal punishment was also ordered from time to time and it was a very salutary way of dealing with little boys who indulged in bag-snatching and other petty crimes. All the subjects were medically examined by me before they were beaten, which was done by the Sergeant-major of the prison warders. Its efficacy was shown by the fact that I never once saw the same boy undergo it a second time. In the case of adults a medical examination was even more necessary because the beating was much more severe. A man who had 20 strokes with a cane was in bed for several days.

An incident in connection with the Prison Hospital will illustrate the way in which departmental discipline was administered and the attitude of the PMO towards his juniors. Across the valley from the prison hospital there was a camp of railway labourers amongst whom several cases of typhoid fever occurred. This was a serious matter and the MO i/c of the camp looked round for a suitable scapegoat. He picked on me and discussing the possible source of the infection with the MOH, he suggested that it might have come from the prison hospital. Dr Johnstone was on leave at the time otherwise the matter would have ended there, but the man who was acting in his place sent a sanitary inspector to look over the prison hospital without first notifying me of his intention. A sanitary inspector's report is always a formidable document and this was no exception. It so happened that there were two cases of typhoid in the hospital at the time, indeed there nearly always were one or more. The mosquito-proof gauze around the isolation ward was defective and the latrines were by no means fly-proof. Both these facts were recorded in the SI's report. Having studied the report the MOH endorsed it;

'It is evident that the supervision exercised by the MO i/c Prison Hospital is negligible and that this was the source from which the labourers in the railway camp were infected.'

I knew all about the holes in the mosquito gauze which were made by friends of the patients in isolation to pass in cigarettes. As fast as one was repaired another was made. I had referred to this matter and to all the other points raised by the SI in repeated letters to the prison authorities sent through the PMO as regulation required. Like everyone else the Commissioner of Prisons was short of money and had done nothing to improve matters. I had however made sure that the patients in the isolation ward passed their stools and urine into vessels containing disinfectant, a fact which had escaped the notice of the sanitary inspector. He had also failed to observe that the prevailing wind blew strongly across the valley from the railway camp. No fly could have flown against it for the required distance of a quarter of a mile.

When the PMO received the report and the covering letter from the MOH, he sent for me and when I went to his office the railway MO was there with him. I had with me my copy of the report as well as my correspondence file, but I was left in no doubt of the fact that I had already been tried and found guilty, so I decided that the best method of defence was attack. I told Dr Gilks that I wished to lodge a formal complaint against the MOH for sending a subordinate officer to inspect my hospital without first notifying me; a gross infringement of the elementary principles of medical etiquette.

Dr Gilks replied that in a disciplined service there was no question of etiquette; a senior man could take any action he thought necessary without consulting his juniors. I told him that if I thought he really meant what he said I should be tempted to resign my appointment forthwith. I said that it seemed incredible to me that the mere accident which had brought one man into the service a few months before his professional brother could absolve him from behaving with ordinary courtesy.

I then referred to the endorsement which had been written at the foot of the report and said that since the MOH had not himself been to confirm the findings of his subordinate he was taking a great deal too much on himself for he was criticizing the PMO who must know from the correspondence which had passed through his hands that though my efforts had been futile, I had done everything in my power to improve conditions at the gaol. I then laid my correspondence file on the desk. 'This,' I said 'is what happens when an officer who only had the power by reason of a few months seniority to do so, ignored the canons of professional behaviour. If I had been present when the SI made his inspection, I could have put him in the picture and in so doing saved the PMO and myself a great deal of embarrassment. I said I was sure that he himself would exact an apology for the slur which had been cast on the efficiency of the Head Office and I hoped that I would also receive one for the unwarranted and unjustifiable censure which I had received. I then turned to the railway MO, told him of the precautions which I took in the isolation ward to prevent any possible spread of infection and pointed out that flies would never travel a quarter-of-a-mile in the face of a prevailing wind. He had the grace to apologize there and then. I was subsequently visited by the Acting MOH who made a somewhat graceless and hesitant apology. The PMO invoked the Public Health Ordinance and stimulated the Commissioner of Prisons to bring the hospital buildings up to standard, but no one ever succeeded in preventing convicts making holes in the mosquito-proof gauze.

With the abolition of slavery, cultivation on the East African littoral plain which was once the granary of Arabia, virtually ceased. The genial climate of the coast is not conducive to physical effort and the local tribes, the Wadigo and the Wagiriama were content to grow just enough crops to stave off starvation and spend the rest of their time basking in the sunshine. Many of these people were the descendants of the slaves who, when they first came to the coast embraced Islam, the religion of their masters.

The climate and terrain were such that infestation with hook-worms was almost universal and Dr Paterson conceived the idea that if the people could be relieved of their parasites they would cease to be so lethargic in their habits and that it would be possible to induce them to grow cash crops thereby improving their standards of living. He decided to mount an anti-hookworm campaign and sent Dr Charles Philip to make a preliminary survey. His choice of Charles Philip was a wise one for he was an exceptional man with a gift of oratory and a wide knowledge of Swahili which enabled him to make the best use of his talents. The first phase having been completed the second followed in natural sequence. The Wadigo must be persuaded to dig pit latrines because it was no use deworming them if their personal habits remained so primitive that re-infection was certain to occur. This was where Charles Philip's eloquence was so valuable. Backed by the District Commissioner, he toured the country for all the world like an evangelist preaching elementary sanitation. When this latrine campaign had been completed there remained the problem of how to carry out mass treatment and with what drug.

This was where I was brought into the picture for it was decided to carry out clinical trials at the Approved School and the gaol in Nairobi. There was a certain Robert Daubney working at the Veterinary Research Laboratory not far from the Approved School and he had already earned for himself an international reputation as a parasitologist. Dr Johnstone took me to see Daubney and it was agreed that since I knew nothing whatever about the practical side of helminthology he would supervise my work. For months I worked in close collaboration with him; he taught me the flotation technique for the recovery of helminth eggs from faeces and explained the difference between the various ova we found.

We began operations by examining the stools of all the boys at the Approved School for hookworm ova and found that quite a number of them were harbouring the parasites. Daubney had previously used carbon tetrachloride as a vermifuge in sheep and found it efficacious and he suggested that it might be even more effective if combined with oil of chenopodium, another anthelminthic. We tried various doses and finally decided that the best mixture was one containing one part of the oil to three parts of the tetrachloride; the dose was 4 ccs for an adult. I now began operations at the gaol and having collected a number of hookworm cases we set out to test the value of our mixture. This meant treating the patients and then collecting, washing and screening all their stools for three days. The stools were collected in earthenware jars which I took out to the Vet Lab in my car each morning, a distance of some ten miles. This was an unsavoury journey and sometimes an embarrassing one because in the days before there was any public transport one never passed a pedestrian without offering a lift and the stench from the back of the car took a bit of explaining.

The outcome of our work was that Daubney and I concluded that we had hit on the best mixture and the right dose and we recommended its use in the Digo campaign. It was laid down that the dose had to be taken on an empty stomach sandwiched between two doses of Epsom salts to minimize absorption. All patients were warned to take no alcohol overnight and to starve until the Epsom salts had done their work. Philip estimated that he treated more than ninety per cent of the entire Digo tribe with two deaths. The two men who died were found to have lined up for their treatment literally in the middle of a beer-drinking orgy; they therefore had no one to blame but themselves.

I personally gained much useful experience from this job of work. Daubney and I wrote a joint paper which was published in 'Parasitology' so that in addition to learning a great deal of practical helminthology I was shown how to compile a scientific treatise and its bibliography. I went on with the work at the prison because I had noticed that our vermifuge mixture not only dealt with hookworms, but also with the beef tapeworm, *Taenia saginata* and I made this the subject of my MD thesis.

For his monumental work Charles Philip was awarded the MBE, but I never heard that the hookworm campaign made any difference to the habitual lethargy of the Wadigo.

In 1928 I went on home leave and served my belated stint at the Tropical School under such teachers as Carmichael Low, Philip Manso-Bahr, Sir Leonard Rogers, Sir Thomas Carey-Evans, Sir Aldo Castellani, Louis Westenra Sambon and P. A. Buxton. Sir Andrew Balfour made me free of his personal library and largely due to this and the help I had had from Daubney, my thesis was accepted and I passed the London MD.

CHAPTER IV

There were several substantial urban communities besides that of
Nairobi and of these the largest and most important was Mombasa
where the shipping companies had their offices. Here there was a
large African hospital as well as a European one which occupied a
singularly beautiful site overlooking the Indian Ocean. Then there
were centres at Naivasha, Nakuru, Kericho, Thika, Nyeri, Kisumu,
Eldoret and Kitale. Most of these places had African hospitals and
Kisumu had a European one as well. In Nakuru and Eldoret there
were European hospitals run by independent committees. In the
African Reserves the aim was to establish a hospital in each
administrative centre and to staff it with at least two MOs so that one
could be on safari paying regular visits to outlying dispensaries while
the other ran the hospital. This ideal object had not yet been
achieved except in one or two instances and in some it never was
achieved at all.

At each administrative centre the officials lived in what was called
the 'boma'. This is a Swahili word which means literally a stockade or
enclosure and its use was a survival of the days when it was necessary
for a group to live inside a protecting wall as a protection from wild
animals or marauding tribesmen. The more modern boma had no
stockade, but simply meant that a group of officials lived together in
juxtaposition. Such a small community would consist of the District
Commissioner, one or more Assistant District Commissioners, the
Veterinary Officer, the Agricultural Officer, the MO and perhaps
one or more nursing sisters, sometimes a member of the Public
Works Department, a prison officer and a policeman. It must not
however be supposed that all these departments were represented in
any except the larger centres and at Provincial Headquarters there
would be a Provincial Commissioner above the DC.

In the average boma the DC was the recognized senior officer and all new arrivals were expected to report to him on arriving in the station. Most of the senior administrative officers with whom I had dealings were delightful people, but some of them 'clothed with a little brief authority' behaved like little tin gods as did also their wives. They had the first call on the services of the prisoners and detainees to tend their gardens and wash their cars and the ladies when they wanted to make up a bridge four expected the invitees to turn up whether they wanted to or not. A Provincial Commissioner was a very exalted personage indeed, being in line for promotion to Chief Native Commissioner and a possible Governorship.

My personal experience of work in a reserve was a little unusual in that I did not live at the District Headquarters so there was no boma at my station and there was no government hospital. I was stationed at Maseno, seventeen miles north of Kisumu and when I arrived in 1929 there were only two other officials, a Veterinary Officer and his Stock Inspector. There was a large CMS secondary school and a CMS hospital which since it received a grant from the Medical Department was subject to my supervision.

When I had landed at Mombasa on my return from leave I found a message awaiting me which said I was to contact Charles Philip before proceeding up country. Prior to taking up his work at the Coast Charles had been stationed at Maseno and he gave me a lot of useful information and advice. In spite of this the task which confronted me was a formidable one. My district which is now called Central Nyanza stretched eastwards to the Uganda border and northwards from the Lake nearly to Mount Elgon. Most of the people belonged to the Jaluo tribe which was of Nilotic origin having invaded the country from the north some four hundred years earlier. To the north and east there were considerable numbers of Bantu Kavirondo who spoke a totally different language and of course had a different origin. Prior to the advent of Christian missionaries the Jaluo people had gone entirely unclothed and in some of the remoter parts of the district they still did. Although they were essentially happy-go-lucky people they were very politically-minded and were regarded as being one of the most progressive tribes in the Colony. Many of them left home to work on farms and estates all over the country and they also made excellent house servants. Physically they were as fine a race as one could wish to meet and took great pleasure in wrestling and playing football.

I had been told that I must bear in mind two main objects in my work at Maseno. One was to try and organize the regular treatment of yaws with metallic bismuth and the other was to promote as far as I could the general bonification of the population, that is to try and improve their standards of living.

In the absence of a hospital my time was spent largely on safari, making regular visits to a chain of dispensaries twelve in number, each sited in one of the locations which made up the District. Since there was no registration of births and deaths no accurate estimate of the population was possible, but it was probably somewhere between 300,000 and a quarter of a million.

My work at the various dispensaries did not differ materially from that of any district MO, so an account of it will serve to give a picture of the conditions which prevailed in the early 1930s. There were however two dispensaries which I visited every week, that in South Gem and that in Alego. This was to make sure that there was continuity in the treatment of cases of yaws and syphilis.

Contrary to popular belief there were no tribal chiefs in East Africa, that is chiefs in the accepted sense of the term as it applies for instance in West Africa. The tribal unit of this patriarchal society was the family and the oldest surviving member of the family was its acknowledged head. Families were grouped together into clans and if one family patriarch outlived all his fellows he would be recognized as the clan leader. Very exceptionally one clan leader might survive all the others and he would then become in effect the Chief of the tribe, though the office was not hereditary and his status died with him. This had happened in my day in the case of North Nyanza where a man called Mumia had lived to a great age. This was shown by the fact that the town of Mumias, properly spelt Mumia's was in being before the British occupation. In C. W. Hobley's book *Kenya from Chartered Company to Crown Colony* there is a picture dated in 1899 which shows Mumia as a man already apparently around fifty years of age. He was recognized by the Administration as the leader of his tribe and when I knew him in 1931 he was still in possession of all his faculties. When he died he was almost certainly a centenarian.

In general a District covered the area inhabited by a tribe or a large part of a tribe and each District was divided into locations. There was a chief over each location, but such men were chosen and appointed by the DC and were usually clan leaders or oldish men held in respect by the community. They were really junior civil servants who fulfilled the functions of magistrates, dealing with petty crime and minor problems involving native laws and customs such as land boundaries, matrimonial disputes and differences about bride-price and the ownership of cattle. The chiefs were also responsible for the collection of hut-tax and for road maintenance. There was one serious objection to the system in that it gave many opportunities for bribery and corruption, opportunities which were not infrequently seized, for the chances of discovery were small.

In my district there were twelve locations and in the nature of things their respective dispensaries were widely separated. In each location the chief held a weekly 'baraza' or conference when the old men gathered in solemn conclave under the baraza tree and deliberated upon the cases which came up for hearing. These barazas were of great value to the various departmental officers who could attend them and address the elders on any subject of topical importance. An MO for instance could make use of these opportunities to speak about anti-malarial measures, methods of preventing plague and sleeping sickness or matters concerning housing and the general standards of living. The elders would listen and then raise any matters which they wished to discuss. In my own case they were deeply concerned about the high rate of infant mortality and I was able to indicate how many of the unhygienic customs followed by the women were largely responsible. Another subject which was often brought up was the rapid spread of syphilis and this they blamed on two things. Firstly they said that before the missionaries came and taught the people to wear clothes, the young men were careful to avoid venereal infection which would be apparent for all to see. The second factor was the introduction of Indian trading centres the owners of which plied back and forth along the country roads in motor lorries driven by Africans. These drivers were in the habit of giving lifts to young girls and accepting payment in kind and this practice was a serious menace to tribal morality.

The most important African consortium was the Local Native Council which met quarterly under the chairmanship of the District Commissioner. Its members were the chiefs and location headmen and certain elected elders. In Central Nyanza this made a large meeting and since the African is *par excellence* an extempore orator and since every member of the Council felt in duty bound to speak on every point raised in debate, meetings were apt to be prolonged. The strain on a Chairman who, having heard the same thing said over and over again sought to prevent so much vain repetition was considerable. The LNC had the power to levy a small local tax or rate over and above the government hut tax and they were allowed to say how this money should be spent, though the DC could veto any suggestion if it were absurd or against the public interest. In Central Nyanza it had been the custom for some years to vote an annual sum for the purchase of NAB because the Medical Department could not afford to supply the drug. The elders were well aware of the efficacy of NAB in yaws and syphilis and spent their money very willingly to buy as much as they could. There was also a small contribution for the purchase of artificial limbs for amputees. I never found out how or why this started because I never knew of a case where the money was needed.

In spite of those who decry the old British Colonial system, it is true to say that by establishing locational and district councils the Administration taught the people a great deal about collective responsibility and mutual help in the community as well as helping them to deal sensibly with public money and I am quite sure that with the coming of independence, this early education has stood the people in good stead. Above and beyond this it must be apparent that this system of central control had a most beneficial effect on the public health and on the control and treatment of disease. No one was quicker to realize these basic truths than the people themselves and they responded during those happier days with enthusiastic co-operation. They saw the Agriculture Officer working hand-in-glove with the Veterinary Officer, and the Education Officer consulting with the MO and they believed that all these people had the interests of their tribe at heart.

In spite of the ceaseless travelling which my work entailed, I should not have found it too arduous had it not been for the appalling state of the roads in wet weather. This was a handicap with which officers all over the Colony had to contend, but it bore more heavily on me for two reasons. Firstly, having no hospital I could not busy myself at my headquarters during the rainy season. To discharge my duties efficiently I had to travel in all weathers throughout the year, even when the DC had declared the roads in the Reserve closed. The other factor was the fact that Central Nyanza was subject at all seasons to sporadic rainstorms. My whole life was conditioned by the fact that these storms tended to occur in the late afternoon when, having finished work at a given dispensary, I was on my way home. There were hardly any bridges and in a few moments a dry gully could become a raging torrent of water impassable to a motor car. The last stage of my homeward journey took me up a long incline over an unmade road the surface of which became glutinous sticky mud soon after it began to rain. My hope was always that I should cross the last water-course and get up that hill before the afternoon downpour started. If I was a little late or if the rain were a bit early I could be delayed for several hours. In dry weather the seventeen mile trip in to Kisumu took a little over half-an-hour, but if it was wet the return journey occupied a whole day. In my first six months at Maseno I completely wore out a set of wheel-chains and I soon learned to carry a large bag of sweets and a carton of cheap cigarettes with which to reward the African men and women who helped to manhandle my car over bad patches of road.

There were inevitably times when my normal routine was upset by some sort of emergency. Plague which was endemic, became epidemic in North Ugenya Location. I wired to Nairobi for supplies of plague vaccine, mobilized my staff, and set to try and cope with the situation. I had a Sanitary Inspector by that time and one or two very competent dressers. I was fortunate in the Chief of North Ugenya, a genial individual with whom I got on very well whenever I visited the local dispensary. He was partial to a glass of sherry and a cigarette and always provided me with a sheep for my staff. He was also very efficient. It used to be said of him that if he woke in the morning after a beer-drink with a sore head, everyone in North Ugenya knew about it before mid-day. In the present emergency he was a tower of strength and by the time the vaccine had arrived he had organized the people so well that all I had to do was to arrange for their injections. Thus it was possible to inoculate the entire population of some 30,000 or 40,000 people in around a fortnight. When we had been at it for a week, all the roads and fields began to be deserted, for the brand of Haffkine plague vaccine put out by the Medical Research Laboratory looked rather like pea soup and gave rise to such formidable reactions that by the time our campaign was finished all the people lay groaning in their huts, wondering which was worse, bubonic plague or the Sirkali's dawa (Government medicine). However in spite of its faults the vaccine was effective and the epidemic was stopped.

In 1931 there came a different kind of emergency when the

36

country suffered an overwhelming invasion of desert locusts. There was a serious risk of famine because to the north, ideal conditions existed for locusts to breed and so the invasion would be sure to last for at least two years. It was essential to try and get the people to plant root crops like sweet potatoes and cassava instead of their usual matama and mwimbi millets. Propaganda to ensure that this was done was part of my duty, but when the hoards of hoppers began to hatch out and spread all over the country, orders were issued that all departmental officers must leave their routine duties and concentrate all their efforts on anti-locust measures. This we did, but it was all rather futile. The numbers of these insects at all stages of their development were so astronomical that it was impossible to make much impression on them. I can still picture a line of villagers facing a swarm of approaching hoppers and swatting them all day long with sticks and branches of trees. When evening came there was a wall of crushed hoppers three feet high and four hundred yards long, but behind it the hoppers still marched on in apparently unreduced numbers. As for an adult swarm, it would be as easy to count the stars in the heavens as it would be to estimate their numbers. I saw one swarm which began its daily flight at around 10.0 a.m. and was so dense that it obscured the light of the tropical sun at noon and this went on until dusk. At nightfall they settled in the trees and their combined weight was so great that throughout the hours of darkness, one could hear the sound of branches breaking under the burden of tens of thousands of insects. On one occasion I was in a train which was halted by locusts; their crushed bodies made the wheels slip on the lines.

Early in the century there had been an epidemic of sleeping sickness on the shores of Lake Victoria, affecting Uganda as well as Kenya and I was ordered to go to Uyoma Location to find out if there were any signs of a recrudescense of the scourge. Uyoma is a peninsula jutting into the Lake from its northern shore and it is to a large degree an isolated unit of the District. When I went there many of the people had never before seen a white man and the majority still went entirely unclothed. There was abundant evidence of the old epidemic in the many deserted villages scattered throughout the bush, but I found very few cases of active trypanosomiasis. Because the people were naturally so shy of me, it was impossible at first to get them to come for examination, but at this time the locust invasion had destroyed so many crops that there was a serious shortage of food. The Chief asked me if I would shoot a hippo to provide his people with some meat and I readily agreed on condition that my requirements as to medical examinations were met. I got what I wanted and he got the meat of three hippos for the people.

It used to be taken for granted that malaria was just malaria and that an attack of sub-tertian fever contracted in Nairobi was no different from one acquired in, for instance, Kisumu. This view had later to be revised and it came to be recognized that the strain of *Plasmodium falciparum* which is met with on the shores of Lake Victoria, is an unusually virulent one. Certainly during my two years at Maseno I was seldom free from malaria and more than once I was re-infected while I was still taking quinine to treat an earlier attack. Incidentally this shows the futility of the old custom of taking a daily dose of quinine as a prophylactic. Blackwater fever was common and was indeed the reason why, having contracted what fortunately proved to be a mild attack I was posted elsewhere at the end of 1931.

I treated a good many cases including several Africans and a Roman Catholic priest who eventually died. His friend Monsignor Brandsma showed his appreciation of my endeavours to save him by issuing instructions to all his mission stations that if ever I was in their vicinity on safari I was to be put up at the presbytery. This was a great convenience, especially in wet weather, and I was often glad to avail myself of the privilege.

From time to time, in order to save life I was forced to perform a surgical operation under primitive conditions. I amputated the arm of a man who had been seized by a crocodile, but had managed to escape and I did a gastrostomy by the light of a petrol lamp on a man who had stuffed himself so full of locusts that he had gastric obstruction. Both these patients made uneventful recoveries.

Some months after I arrived in Maseno, my staff was augmented, first by a Sanitary Inspector and then by a junior MO. Both of these officers were married so our little community was doubled in size; soon it was more than doubled because both of the wives had babies. The Sanitary Inspector started demonstration centres where the Africans were shown how to make sun-dried bricks and drain-pipes. They were also taught how to enclose the head-waters of streams and so lead the flow to raised positions where a vessel could be filled directly instead of scooping the water up from a muddy pool. Another project which proved in the end to be of little practical value was to popularize building in pisé-de-terre. To demonstrate the advantages of improved methods of building and encourage the people to adopt them, a model village was built at Maseno. Here were erected single and two-roomed houses in brick, pisé-de-terre and well-designed and properly-constructed huts with beautifully thatched roofs.

Visiting Africans were taken to see the model village and harangued by the SI or the Head Dresser on the virtues of living in decent houses which could be kept clean. They listened and accepted all this, but they could not accept the idea that the Government had built all these lovely houses just to look at, especially when they knew that the quarters of my own staff at Maseno were vastly inferior. I wrote to Dr Paterson and explained this very logical viewpoint to him, but he was very disinclined to allow his immaculate model village to be lived in. I persevered however, and in the end I got him to consent since as I pointed out, a model village inhabited by model people would have much more propaganda value. It goes without saying that I made sure that the village was kept up to the proper standards.

From time to time senior officers from Medical Headquarters paid visits of inspection to out-stations and a small incident will serve to illustrate one facet of Dr Paterson's interesting personality. His designation had now been changed to Deputy Director of Sanitary Services, while Dr Gilks was no longer PMO, he was now Director of Medical and Sanitary Services. Paterson was of all things an enthusiast and he was very keen on all aspects of African bonification. He had issued a wise directive that all MOs should encourage the cultivation of fruit trees and that they should also plant trees around all dispensaries. I had implemented this order in my District and orange, lemon and gum trees were beginning to flourish at all the dispensaries with one exception. In Samia, up near the Uganda border, I had been quite unable to get any trees to grow; all my repeated efforts to do so failed and when Paterson came on a tour of inspection he at once noticed and commented on the absence of trees at Samia. He demanded an explanation. I told him of my persistent endeavours and explained that in that area there was a small red ant which ate off the bark of young trees just below the surface of the ground. The Agricultural Officer who knew about this ant, made one or two suggestions, but confessed that he himself had been defeated. I tried applying various toxic substances to the stems of the young trees, but all to no purpose, the ants seemed to thrive on them, so I was finally forced to give up. There was evidence that my efforts had always been doomed to failure because the surrounding country was almost innocent of indigenous trees. Paterson was totally unmoved by any of my arguments.

'There is an answer to every question.' He said. 'You must find the answer to this one.'

Of course this trite statement was a fallacy, for it is by no means axiomatic that there is an answer to every question. In later years Paterson found this out when he made an abortive attempt to irrigate the Tana River valley and found that water will not run uphill and when he tried to make the nomadic cattle-loving Masai keep chickens.

From what has been said the reader should have gained an impression of the multifarious character of the reserve MO's duties. He was a clinician, a lecturer in eugenics, a Medical Officer of Health, an educationalist and an amateur agriculturalist. In each boma, as I have stated, the DC was the administrative leader unless the PC happened to live there too. Every newly-arriving officer had to report to him in twenty four hours and thereafter to keep him informed as to his movements. This was only reasonable because in each of these small and often isolated communities someone had to be the boss and the obvious choice was the DC who was always a magistrate, just as the MO was automatically gazetted MOH. Some DCs, fortunately few in numbers, let their power turn their heads and they became miniature despots, much to the discomfort of the other people in the boma over whom they could impose their will in a dozen different ways if they so chose, but still worse, if the DC's wife was so strong-willed as to dominate her husband she could rule the roost in no uncertain manner.

In Maseno where there was no boma this sort of problem did not arise, but it was far otherwise with one of my colleagues. The DC in his boma was a martinet and his wife was a female dragon. Whereas the official working day began at 8.30 a.m., this DC liked to start work at 7 o'clock and he tried to make all the other departmental officials do the same. Most of them took the line of least resistance and did so, but the MO refused and continued to turn up at the hospital at the usual time. The DC countered by ordering that all sentences of corporal punishment should be carried out at 6 o'clock. Since by law the MO had to be present when anyone was beaten, he had to turn up at the prison to examine the subjects before they were caned. There was another way in which the DC made himself unpopular. He had a penchant for grilled kidneys which he enjoyed eating for breakfast with his bacon and eggs and he told the local Somali butcher that all sheep's kidneys were to be reserved exclusively for him. This was a piece of petty tyrannical selfishness which took no account of the fact that other people might also like an occasional kidney for breakfast.

The MO, who like the famous character in one of Kipling's books was a man of infinite resource and sagacity, consulted with his sanitary inspector, one of whose duties was to inspect all carcases slaughtered by the butcher, to ensure that the meat was fit for human consumption. There followed a remarkable incidence of kidney disease amongst the sheep slaughtered and most regrettably all their kidneys had to be condemned. The DC had to go without his favourite breakfast dish and though no doubt he had his suspicions as to what was going on, he could do nothing about it, not being an expert in the examination of meat and knowing that he could not dare to question the validity of the SI's findings.

This state of things continued for some time and the little comedy went on being played until the DC could stand his deprivation no longer and capitulated. He said nothing directly to the doctor, but he changed the time of the morning beatings from 6.0 to 8.0 a.m. and the epidemic of ovine renal tuberculosis cleared up as if by magic. What was even more to the point, he no longer cornered the entire supply of kidneys.

This may all seem so childish as to be almost incredible, but I can vouch for the truth of the story and I could cite others just as unbelievable. It does however illustrate the fact that the lordly DC could not always ride roughshod over the humble MO. Apart from other considerations there were times when a man might need a medical certificate to extend his tour for family or other reasons and when this happened he was completely at the mercy of the MO who could usually find a good excuse for witholding it.

CHAPTER V

Very little is known about the medicaments used by African medicine men and this as will be seen is hardly surprising. The great majority of Africans are as ignorant on the subject as are the Europeans who are interested in it.

From earliest times religion and medicine have been closely associated and the further one travels back over the centuries, the closer this association is found to be. In mediaeval Europe it was the monks who cared for the health of the people and in ancient Egypt it was the priests. In the Old Testament Scriptures the priest was represented as being both a diagnostician and a prognostician, though he appears to have done little or nothing in the field of therapeutics.

Thus to understand the principles which underlie the practice of primitive African medicine one must know something of the religious beliefs which are held by the people. With advancing civilization much of what follows will already have been irrelevant and it may be that some of the facts if they are not recorded may be lost for all time.

It has been said that the more one finds out about a man and his mentality, the less one knows; this paradox would be better expressed by saying that the more one learns about him, the more one realizes that there is a great deal left to learn. If it is true to say that it is given to few if any white men to understand the mind of the African, would it not be equally true to say that the tortuous workings of the white man's mind are just as incomprehensible to his black brother? Let us try to probe a little into some of the mysteries of African religious beliefs.

When white men who were often far from conducting their lives on Christian lines first went to Africa, they were wont to refer to all those of the people who had not embraced Islam as pagans. The dictionary tells us that a pagan is a heathen or an unenlightened person. Anyone who has seen a Masai warrior, spear in hand, standing on a hillock praying with uplifted face to his God would find it difficult to apply such a definition to such a man. Untutored he may be, but unenlightened he certainly is not and who would be bold enough to say that the God to whom his supplications are addressed is not the same God we worship? There is no question here of idolatry; I never once saw an idol during all the years which I spent in Kenya, yet it is certain that most, if not all the tribes in East Africa believe in some kind of supreme being corresponding to a God. In Kikuyu he is called N'gai and is believed to live amongst the snows of Mount Kenya. Sometimes there are two gods, one good and one evil, but is this not true of Christianity which teaches that God the all-loving father is the essence of goodness while the devil Satan rules supreme over the powers of darkness? The main difference is that whereas the Christian deity is thought of as a personal God who cares for us as individuals, the tribal is impersonal and so remote as to be almost, if not quite inaccessible, so that in most tribes, the Masai being a notable exception, no one would ever dream of approaching him directly in prayer. A sceptic might even argue that such a God is more spiritual than the Christian Jehovah.

In what then did the religion of the average tribesman consist? He believes that the destinies of men were controlled by a multitude of spirits, some friendly, some inimical and it is to propitiate these beings and to avoid displeasing them that his efforts were directed. He was hedged about, day and night by a host of 'things to be done and things not to be done'.

The most important spirits are the ancestral ones, 'N'goma' to the Wakikuyu and 'Aimu' to the Wakamba, but there are also spirits which reside in trees and rivers and there are other disembodied spirits which usually tend to be malignant in character and can enter the bodies of men, snakes and other animals as well.

The conception of what the nature of an ancestral spirit is exactly like and whence it derives its substance, varies widely from tribe to tribe. In the case of the Jaluo, the spirit is thought of as being an exact replica in miniature of the dead person as he was at the time of his demise. These little people are some nine to twelve inches in height and it used to be the custom to build small huts for them inside the village enclosure. These afforded them shelter in inclement weather and were also used for offerings of food drink or tobacco for the use of the dear departed. This is in curious and direct contrast to another old custom. It was common if not universal, in former days to bury a dead man under the floor of his hut and before the grave was filled in a wide-bored stalk of 'olengi' grass was put into or near the corpse's mouth and led up to the surface so preserving a downward channel. Whenever his surviving male relatives held a beer-drinking party in the hut, they would open the proceedings by solemnly pouring a little beer down the hollow stalk to refresh the dead man's spirit. If, however his spirit was elsewhere enjoying a separate miniature existence, this would appear to have been a work of supererogation.

Since the spirit was supposed to be a small replica of the body at the time of death, certain important medical, or rather surgical implications became involved. People would go to any lengths to avoid having an amputation performed lest by so doing they condemned themselves to eternal maiming.

I mentioned above having performed an amputation on a man who had been seized by a crocodile. He was brought to my Alego dispensary one afternoon, supported, almost carried by two companions, with his left arm wrapped in cloths which were dripping with blood. The story was that he and the other two men had been washing some clothes at the edge of a small lake when a crocodile which had been hiding in the rushes suddenly grabbed him by the arm just below the elbow. It began to drag him into the water, but his friends were able to take hold of his other arm and there ensued a tug-o'-war like that described by Kipling in his tale of how the elephant got his trunk. Eventually the disappointed crocodile gave up the struggle and returned to its lair.

When I unwrapped the injured limb I found that almost every shred of soft tissue had been stripped off leaving the two bones of the forearem bare down to the wrist. It was manifest that the only possible treatment was immediate amputation, but the man obstinately refused to have this done even when I assured him that the alternative was gangrene and death. No argument of mine or of my more enlightened African staff made the least impression on him.

A diversion was created by the arrival of the patient's father and when the position was explained to him he pondered for a few minutes and then came up with a practical solution. He said that the arm should be cut off, but it must then be thoroughly dried in the sun, wrapped in cloth and stowed safely away in his son's hut. When the man eventually died, the dried arm could be buried with him and that thereafter it would reunite with his body and all would be well. The son agreed to this and I did the amputation with excellent results.

The same difficulty arose in the case of women dying in advanced pregnancy. The notion of their spending eternity great with child was naturally repugnant to their relations and more than once I was asked to perform post mortem Caesarian section so that misfortune could be avoided.

It was the bounden duty of a dead man's surviving male relatives to provide for his welfare and comfort in the spirit world. Failure to do so was sure to be followed by some disaster and this is one reason why Africans are so keen on engendering male children so that they could be sure of a comfortable spirit life. The same desire is found in the Chinese who are, of course ancestor-worshippers and wish for male rather than female children.

Before western influences began to make themselves felt, the lives of African people were ruled by a multitude of regulations to infringe which was to court disaster, of one kind or another and the only education of children and boys in particular was designed to familiarize them with these laws and their observance. They were, however, so multitudinous that no ordinary person could learn about all of them so fully as to be always sure that he had not broken one or other of them. The belief was commonly held that such transgression, resented by the spirits could result in physical ailments. All kinds of illnesses were attributed to this cause so that it now becomes apparent how closely religion and medicine were linked together in the African mind. By far the worst retribution which could be visited on a man was for his wife to be barren or subject to habitual abortion. A man's cattle could also be afflicted in these same two ways and that was nearly as bad. Alternatively his crops might fail, but whatever the cause or effect, the remedy was to call in the medicine man.

These were called in Swahili, *Waganga*, M'ganga in the singular, and they were so well versed in every detail of tribal law that by careful questioning and other means they could always find out how when and in what way a man had been at fault. They were in fact, both legal and medical consultants. They knew what remedies were required in any given case and how they should be applied. The

M'ganga was a legitimate practitioner who practised his profession in the broad light of day and charged the appropriate fee for his services. True he indulged in what we should call 'white magic'; he cast the bones, sacrificed animals, usually fowls and drew conclusions from the appearance of the entrails, thereby reaching a diagnosis. He dealt in herbal remedies and his leaves, fruits and roots had to be collected under the prescribed auspicious circumstances known only to him and their action required to be enhanced by suitable secret incantations at the right phase of the moon. The reason for all this is not far to seek. Anyone could go out into the bush and collect the same bits and pieces, but only the *M'ganga* knew how to render them truly efficacious. Since the profession was highly respected and very profitable, and since one witch doctor was ignorant of the secrets of his colleagues, these same secrets were passed down from father to son so that the office tended to become hereditary.

There can be no doubt that some of the medicines used had some value, particularly in such simple conditions as diarrhoea and constipation and if a given *M'ganga* knew of one or two really effective herbs and used them to advantage, he might acquire such an enhanced reputation that he stood out above his fellows. Such a man would be consulted by the tribal Elders in times of general rather than personal misfortune; drought, famine, epidemic disease, whether of man or cattle and locust invasion, or in bygone days, defeat in battle. He would then stage a truly impressive ceremony at which, assisted by a number of lesser *Waganga,* he would divine the cause of the trouble and prescribe the appropriate sacrifice. So far as I was able to discover there was never any question of human sacrifice in any of the East African tribes and I am sure that such a practice would have been abhorent to the people. Various animals had greater or lesser degrees of virtue as propitiatory sacrifices, but by far the most effective was a black bull.

Distinct altogether from the *M'ganga* and never to be confused with him is the *M'chawi.* This is the repellant witch doctor of such popular works of fiction as those of Rider Haggard and Edgar Wallace. An *M'chawi* is decidedly a person to be avoided at all costs. There is an interesting passage in C. W. Hobley's book *Kenya from Chartered Company to Crown Colony* which aptly pinpoints the difference between an *M'chawi* and a *M'ganga.*

. . . one may . . . suddenly meet an old man decked up in curious

46

ornaments and carrying a basket in which are a number of small gourds each stoppered with a bung made out of the dried tail of an animal . . . and say to himself, 'I have found a real magician!' . . . but it is not so simple as that for the man who walks openly in this fashion is almost certainly only a medical practitioner of a primitive kind . . . The real dispenser of black magic rarely advertises himself; he may be one of the most intelligent Elders who regularly attends the tribal council, or he may be an apparently insignificant old man who lives with his family in an isolated part of the country. The real difficulty in locating these practitioners is the conspiracy of silence which exists regarding their identity.

Thus the *M'ganga* walks freely abroad in the light of the noonday sun while the *M'chawi* weaves his dark spells furtively at dead of night in the secret depths of the forest, contrary to every canon of African custom which abhors the works of darkness and welcomes the genial light of day.

Of course the materialistic sceptic will scoff at magic, black or white, but let him spend a score or so of years in intimate personal contact with primitive people and he may well change his mind and agree with the old Latin tag *Semper ex Africa, aliquid novi.* Has a wizard any occult power? Can he weave a spell and can such a spell be effective? I will try to answer this question by recounting some personal experiences.

Shortly after I arrived in Kenya and long before I had any notions, preconceived or otherwise on the subject of witchcraft, I was staying in a log cabin on the fringe of the Aberdare mountains. We were miles away from the nearest shops and my wife needed some fresh meat. She asked me to try and shoot a buck so I set off in the afternoon with a Kikuyu gun-bearer to try my luck. After walking through the forest for a couple of hours, I had the good fortune to shoot a young bush-buck, one of the so-called 'harness antelopes', the flesh of which is very good eating. We cut down a young sapling, trimmed it and after tying the buck's legs together and slinging his body on the pole, we set off to return home. Night was beginning to fall though we made good progress, but the buck was heavy and when we came to a large open glade on the edge of which lay a fallen tree, I called a halt. I sat down on the tree-trunk and took out my cigarette case to have a smoke while I rested for a while. When I lit a match, it immediately went out although there was no breath of wind stirring. I tried again with the same result and a third attempt was no more successful: I began to feel vaguely uneasy. My gun-bearer said something to me in Kikuyu which I could not understand and pointed to a gigantic parasitic fig tree which stood on the far side of the clearing, then he said in broken English, 'Bad place, no can smoke here, come away.' He again pointed to the fig tree and I went over to have a look at it. The moon had risen by this time and its silvery light was shining directly on the base of the tree-trunk. I saw there a circle of fire-blackened stones and as I stood looking at them, I gradually became aware of an overwhelming sense of evil while the air seemed to grow dank and chill. I was filled with a nameless fear. Was I the subject of auto-suggestion? I cannot say, but I do know that I began to tremble, my knees grew weak and I was in danger of falling to the ground, when my man seized my arm and dragged me away. We picked up our load and set out again. After a little while we came to another, smaller glade where again there was a convenient tree-trunk on which to sit. 'All right to rest here Bwana' said my gun-bearer, so I once again took out my cigarettes and lit one with the first match I struck.

When I arrived home I called my Swahili servant Simba and told him what had happened; could he explain it? He consulted with the gun-bearer and then told me that the place where I had first tried to rest was where the Kikuyu *Wachawi* met at night to sacrifice to evil spirits; I had seen the remains of their last fire. Simba, being a Swahili was, of course, a Muslim and a very devout one and I asked him if he believed in all this mumbo-jumbo. 'Oh yes Bwana.' He said, 'these people worship the Devil. We believe in the Devil just as you do and it is best to have nothing to do with him or his servants.' I asked him what would have happened if I had not left when I did, but he shook his head and said he could not say; he himself had never been to such a place and had no desire to do so.

Years later in Central Nyanza I was asked to go and see a man who was lying very ill in bed. He was indeed in a bad way so I took a blood smear and made a thorough physical examination, but I could find no signs of organic disease. The blood-slide was negative. My Head-dresser, Ismail Owuoth told me that the man's relatives believed him to have been bewitched and that if they were right he would surely die. When I questioned the patient, he told me the same story. He had no symptoms, no pain, only an increasing feeling of weakness

48

and he died that same night. In the circumstances I insisted on doing an autopsy and contrary to their usual obstructive attitude when this was suggested, the people seemed even anxious that I should carry on. It was not possible to open the skull or vertebrae to examine the brain and spinal cord, but apart from that I did a pretty thorough post mortem. Nowhere did I find any evidence of organic disease. I think that if there had been any central nervous condition, I should have detected it in my physical examination and the possibility of a fatal cerebral haemorrhage was remote because the man had not succumbed to a sudden illness. I asked Ismail what he thought about it and he assured me that it was a simple matter of greed. There had been two brothers, the elder of whom was rich in cattle and was the father of the dead man. He had no other sons and was not expected to live much longer. The younger brother had one son who, since his father had died years before, had by this untimely death of his childless cousin, become heir to all his uncle's wealth. Ismail said nothing more, but had he known of it, he might have quoted the Latin proverb *Verbum sapientis sufficit*.

I have already mentioned that the Elders of the Central Nyanza Local Native Council voted an annual sum for the purchase of NAB to be used in the treatment of yaws and syphilis. I kept all the stocks of this drug under lock and key at Maseno, but when I visited outlying dispensaries I took supplies with me and issued it to the local dressers an ampoule at a time for use in the most suitable cases; the less severe ones were given courses of injections with metallic bismuth, but they were all very well aware of the superior efficacy of NAB. Several of the dressers had, unknown to me, taken to giving less than the prescribed dose, making one ampoule do for two patients. In this way they built up a private stock of the drug which they then sold at exorbitant prices. Ismail Owuoth had discovered this and, as was his duty, had reported it to me. I could not sack the culprits, but they were fined and I stopped their little game by giving all the intravenous injections myself. One day Ismail came to me and told me that one of the disappointed dressers, he did not know which, had had him bewitched in revenge.

'But Ismail,' I said, 'you are a Christian, surely you don't believe in witchcraft?'

'Bwana,' he replied, 'I only know that day by day I grow weaker and soon I shall die.'

He then produced a small bundle of twigs and laid it on my desk.

49

'This is the spell,' he told me, 'it was hidden in the thatch above the door of my hut and it has done its work.'

He explained that if a man consulted an *M'chawi* in order to get rid of an enemy, he would be told to get hold of some part of the proposed victim's body; the clippings of his hair, his nail-parings, the bristles of his beard, or even a fragment of his faeces. The *M'chawi* would wrap the material in a special leaf, enclose the leaf in a small bundle of twigs and tie it up like a miniature faggot. At night, in the depths of the forest, he would invoke the evil spirits and after sacrificing to them invest the spell with magical powers. The spell had to be so placed that the person to be bewitched would pass over or under it several times; it would affect no one else. It might, as in this case be hidden in the roof of the hut, or it might be put in a hole dug in the path leading to the door. It would then exert its sinister power and the result was quite inevitable.

Ismail then told me that the only remedy was to have the *M'chawi* who had cast the spell, reverse it and begged me to see that this was done.

I gave a good deal of thought to the matter and finally I called my entire African staff to a meeting at Maseno. I told them that one of them had certainly arranged for Ismail Owuoth to be bewitched and showed them the spell. I went on to say that I knew very well that it would be futile for me to question them, since the culprit would not confess and I, a white man could not tell who was lying and who was telling the truth. I then told them that I possessed the secret of a medicine far more powerful than any they had ever dreamed of and I produced a mug containing the most disgusting mixture I had been able to concoct in the dispensary. I placed this on the desk in front of me and recited over it some lines of Latin verse which I had written out.

'Now,' I told them, 'each one of you will repeat the words which I tell you and then drink some of my medicine.'

I stood them up in line and presented the mug to each in turn, telling them to swear;

'I am innocent of this crime and if I am lying, may this medicine kill me.'

I passed down the line and each man took the oath and drank from the cup until one of them said the medicine smelled foul and he would not drink it. I made no comment and passed on. All the others took the oath and I then called out the non-drinker and gave him a second chance. Once again he refused. There were about thirty men present and I appealed to them to declare who was guilty. Their verdict was unanimous.

The Native Affairs Department was well aware of the existence of *Wachawi* and recognized that they had power to kill people by magic. A Witchcraft Ordinance had been drawn up and it provided for the death penalty to be imposed in such cases. I told my culprit that he had two alternatives. Either he could pay his *M'chawi* to reverse the spell, or I should take him to Kisumu and hand him over to the DC. Then when Ismail died he would be tried for murder and executed. He chose the former course, but bewailed the fact that the wizard would demand an even higher fee for removing the spell than he had done for making it in the first place. That, I told him was his look-out. He took the spell and went away. I don't know how many cows or goats it cost him, but he must have done as he was told because Ismail Owuoth's health rapidly improved and he was soon back to normal. The sceptic will say that the whole thing could be explained by auto-suggestion, but I wonder!

Another case might have had more serious repercussions. At this time there was a good deal of subversive political activity in Central Nyanza, largely fostered by that redoubtable cleric Archdeacon Owen, the acknowledged champion of the downtrodden. There was a sharp division between the conservative element which resisted the march of civilization and the more liberal-minded who favoured progress. There was a highly-respected Chief in North Gem Location named Ogada who belonged to the latter faction. Ogada had accepted Christianity, but had not been baptized because he declined to repudiate his wives of which he had six. I personally respected him for his loyalty to his family, but the CMS authorities were adamant. At all events Ogada co-operated whole heartedly with the Government in all its plans for the welfare of the people and thereby incurred the emnity of the conservatives.

The day came when it was reported to me that Ogada had been taken ill and I went to see him. He was not in bed but he looked a very sick man. When I examined him the only thing I found was that there were a few doubtful physical signs at the apex of one lung which could have been the result of a healed tuberculous lesion. Certainly there was no active disease and no cough. I had brought a microscope and its accessories with me and I took, stained and examined a blood-slide. After a prolonged and careful search I failed to find a single malaria parasite, or for that matter any evidence of some other blood disease. When I had finished, Ogada smiled wanly and told me I was wasting my time because he was bewitched. My experience had by now taught me to take this sort of statement very seriously and I drove to Kisumu and laid the facts before the Provincial Commissioner who was a very knowledgeable officer and held Ogada in high regard. He also had met plenty of cases of bewitchment and he shared my concern. He left his office and accompanied me back to Ogada's village where he at once convened a baraza of all the Location Elders. He did not beat about the bush, but stated categorically that Ogada had been bewitched and that there was no time to institute a search for the guilty party. He then said that he would exact a fine of one tenth of all the cattle in North Gem unless the person responsible for the crime were produced within twenty-four hours. This was a most formidable threat and it affected every single man in the Location, but the Elders knew that the PC had the power to carry it out and that he would not hesitate to do so.

In this instance no single individual was responsible, but a group had conspired together. One of them ratted on his fellows and in the end they all confessed. They were then ordered to produce the *M'chawi*, but this they said they could not do, though they promised to consult with him and arrange for the spell on Ogada to be lifted. When they saw the wizard he told them that the spell was a very powerful one which could only be reversed by the sacrifice of a black bull which must not have one single white hair on its body. Such an animal was not easy to find, but eventually one was discovered and it was purchased by the PC out of Local Native Council funds and handed over. The ceremony of disenchantment was performed and Chief Ogada recovered.

The last story which I have to relate concerns devil-possession and though I never personally saw the subject the account was given to me at first hand by one of the participants in the drama. Those who are familiar with the New Testament cannot have failed to notice that whereas some of the miracles performed by our Lord were manifestly on epileptics, others quite specifically concerned cases of demoniacal possession. To those who have faith in the inspiration of the Holy Scriptures, what follows will not be difficult to believe. I personally believe every word of it and it was told me by the Reverend Pitt-Pitts, Chaplain to the Bishop of Mombasa.

After the 1914–1918 war while British troops were still stationed in Uganda, a certain officer became deeply interested in the subject of black magic and made contact with some Africans who practised the cult. He frequently met with them and one day he told his fellow officers that he was to be initiated into their inner mysteries that night. He left the mess after dinner.

In the morning he had not returned to his quarters and when he had not returned at lunch time a search party was sent out and found him wandering about in the bush violently insane. He had to be secured and forcibly restrained and since there was no provision in Uganda for the treatment of such cases he was sent under guard to the Mathari Mental Hospital at Nairobi.

With the passage of time the patient began to have lucid intervals and whenever this happened he asked to see a minister of the Church of England. This was eventually arranged through the Bishop of Mombasa and my friend Pitt-Pitts went to see the man. Pitt-Pitts told me that the patient gave him a detailed account of what had happened that night in the forest, but the ceremony was so foul that he could not bring himself to tell me about it. The patient then told him that he was possessed by a demon and since Pitt-Pitts professed to be the servant of One who not only could cast out devils himself, but enjoined his followers to do so, he wanted Pitt-Pitts to do just that for him.

As Pitt-Pitts told me, he found himself in something of a quandary. The man was a certified lunatic and the whole thing might be a delusion of his disordered mind and moreover he had no experience in such matters and had no idea how to go about it. However, he prayed with the man and left.

The patient's condition was now static, alternating between bouts of maniacal frenzy and periods of complete normality, during which Pitt-Pitts visited him several times. He made no further progress and then one day with tears running down his face he again besought Pitt-Pitts to cast out his devil. Pitt-Pitts told me that quite suddenly he felt an imperious urge to act, so he rose to his feet, stretched out his hand and cried,

'In the name of the Lord Jesus Christ, Come out of him!'

Immediately the man fell down in a violent convulsive fit and Pitt-Pitts hurriedly rang the bell for help. The attendant came, the fit passed and the two of them lifted the still unconscious man on to his bed. Restoratives were applied and after a time the patient recovered

53

his senses and held out his hand to Pitt-Pitts.

'Thank you Padre,' he said, 'I shall be all right now.'

From that day forward there were no more attacks of mania and in due course the patient was discharged from hospital and sent back to England.

Even in modern times it was possible to find in remote parts of Europe, people who are were-wolves and the same concept is found in Africa, where leopard men seek out their victims and kill them by night. Belief is also rife on the subject of the evil eye, not only in Europe but in Morocco and other parts of Africa. In Africa there are a few people who possess this attribute; they are born with it and it tends to be hereditary. A man may admire one of his neighbour's cows and if he does so more than once and the animal subsequently sickens and dies, the man will be credited with having the evil eye. The misfortune can be averted if the man moistens his finger and touches the beast on the mouth and other parts of the body. This malign glance can cause a woman to abort or it can give rise to inflammation of the breasts; inanimate objects can be marred or broken and only the one who caused the damage can prevent it. The medicine man is powerless to help.

No one who is not born with this power can acquire it; it is a gift from God, a misfortune which cannot be avoided though many of the persons concerned have not the least desire to harm anyone or anything. When such a man enters a village, he will be asked in a friendly way to spit upon all the children or to anoint any cattle which may be there on their mouths with spittle. There is no explanation as to why saliva should be held to act as such an efficient prophylactic.

Magical charms also merit attention they are many and varied. One used to see little square skin pouches hanging round nearly everyone's neck. They were black with the sweat of years and contained medicine against all sorts of ills. Some of the Wakamba wore little cylindrical rods of wood at the elbow to ward off the effects of snake-bite.

A phenomenon which is not easy to understand is self-immolation. After all self-preservation is credited with being man's strongest instinct. From time to time one heard tentative references to such cases, but I only had personal experience of one. There was a European settler who owned an estate a few miles outside Nairobi where, as was common practice he maintained a small dispensary for the treatment of minor ailments in his labour force. One of his men developed an intractable tropical ulcer on his leg and when it failed to respond to the usual remedies, he asked his master to take him to the hospital in Nairobi. This was agreed to, but for one reason or another it was repeatedly postponed. At last the labourer confronted his master and told him that he did not believe that he had any intention of keeping his promise. The settler assured him that he was mistaken and promised that the very next time he went to Nairobi he would certainly take him to the hospital. When the day came the car was ready and the man was sitting in it and they were just about to leave when a message was brought from a neighbour to say that his car had broken down and it was imperative for him and his wife to go to Nairobi that morning. This meant that there would be no room for the man with the ulcer and he was told to get out.

'Once more you have broken your promise.' he cried, 'I know that you will never take me.'

The car left and when the farmer returned and he and his wife went to enter their house, the dead body of the labourer was lying stretched out across the threshold. It was his belief that this act would give him power to haunt his master and bring misfortune on him and his family.

Antidotes against snake-bite are not rare and C. W. Hobley in his *Bantu Beliefs and Magic*, devotes a good deal of space to the subject. I am indebted to his book for most of what follows. He gives a detailed account of the ingredients of a medicine used by the Wakamba of Machakos.

Certain herbs were collected, dried and placed in a pot and to them was added the head of a snake. Before the snake's head was severed, a number of gashes were made on it with a knife and some cuts were also made on the medicine man's hand. The human and snake blood were mixed and added to the pot and after more drying the whole was pounded up to make a black powder. If a person was to be immunized, cuts were made at his wrist, elbow, shoulder and tongue, on the top of the foot, the thigh and the buttock. This was done on both sides of the body and then the *M'ganga* takes some of the powder in the palm of his right hand, dips the tip of the second finger of his left hand in it and transfers some to each of the wounds. The patient then licks the residue of the powder off his hand. The man so treated is then immune to snake-bite and this was proved to

Hobley by a practical demonstration. One such man, having heard that poisonous snakes were needed for experimentation, brought in a large puff adder which had already bitten him. Hobley saw this man catch and handle several venomous snakes. He would put his hand quite fearlessly into the holes of ant-hills where snakes commonly lie up and withdraw puff adders and cobras in spite of their bites.

In Tanganyika there is a small community of so-called 'snake-men' who are immune to snake-bites and can cure them in others.

In former days Masai warriors frequently went for long distances on forays, killing other tribesmen and driving off their cattle. These long journeys were made at a jog-trot and sometimes lasted for days on end. The Masai may still have occasion to make long journeys, though for more peaceful purposes and when they do they can go for days without food and apparently without fatigue. A friend of mine, an Assistant District Commissioner, once saved the life of a young *el-moran* who was attacked by a lion and in conversation with this man he remarked upon the remarkable powers of endurance possessed by members of his tribe. The man told him that they had the secret of a medicine which they chewed when they travelled for long distances and in gratitude for what had been done for him, he agreed to give the ADC a quantity of this substance. He fulfilled his promise and produced a bundle of what looked like dried roots. This was sent to England for examination and pharmacological tests. No active ingredients were found and all the tests were negative. So the vaunted medicine was proved to be valueless; or was it that the young Masai, rather than reveal a jealously-guarded tribal secret had given the ADC a useless bundle of roots instead of the real thing?

Whatever may be said of the virtues or otherwise of African medicines, there can be no doubt of the efficacy of Giriama arrow poison. The Wagiriama prepare this from the fruit of the tree *Strophanthus hispidus* or from that of *Strophanthus kombe,* which is mixed with a number of other ingredients which are probably quite useless. The mixture is pounded up with water and then boiled until it has the consistency of thick glue and this on cooling congeals into a sticky black mass which can be smeared on an arrow-head. The Wagiriama used to carry on, and possibly still do, a very profitable export trade with the Wakamba who are notorious elephant-poachers. It is doubtful whether poisoned arrows were ever used in inter-tribal warfare. Once when I was on a hunting safari with a Game Warden, one of his scouts caught a Giriama man who was carrying some of the poison. It was in round lumps the size of a cricket ball and each was enclosed in a wicker-work covering.

The elephant hunter will stalk an animal, preferably an old bull carrying heavy ivory and getting close to it, perhaps even under its body, flick an arrow upwards to pierce the relatively thin skin of its abdomen. This may sound fanciful, but I have myself seen a Wasanya hunter crawl beneath an elephant, stand up and tickle its tummy with the tip of his finger. Of course the wind had to be in the right direction and of course the great beast could not bend down and look to see what it was he felt and he would think it was a twig stirring in the breeze.

Strophanthin, the active principle of the *Strophanthus* fruit, is a very powerful cardiac alkaloid, the human dose of which is half a milligram, an amount which would be vastly succeeded by the amount of poison smeared on an arrow. If the poison is fairly fresh and the arrow penetrates the skin, the elephant will move off and walk for about half-an-hour, then it will stand still for another couple of hours, after which it will topple over and quickly die. After three days in the hot sun there will be enough decomposition for the tusks to be pulled out and the hunter has earned his reward while the Lord of the Jungle has provided him with the wherewithal to pay the bride-price of another wife.

CHAPTER VI

Prior to my leaving Nairobi, several new doctors had joined the ranks of the general practitioners, including Dr W. G. S. Hopkirk who joined Gerald Anderson and later qualified himself as a highly competent radiologist; he is still in active practice. Drs Boyle and Guy Johnson also joined Gerald, but they left him later because of a divergence of opinion about Gerald's sincerely-held belief in the teaching of the Oxford Group Movement.

When I returned after four years absence I found many changes and newcomers; the most important of these latter being Dr J. H. Sequeira of the London Hospital who had been a pioneer in the fields of radiology and the Finsen light treatment of tuberculosis of the skin. He was in charge of the Department of Dermatology at the London, but like Dr Jex-Blake had been advised for health reasons to go and live in a more genial climate. He chose to come to Kenya because his adopted son had a farm at Makuyu and he went there to live, but he came regularly to Nairobi where he soon built up a consulting practice. Dr Sequeira came of a long and uninterrupted line of medical men and he was very proud of the fact. An ancestor of his was Court Physician to the King of Portugal who lent him to King Charles II. The merry monarch took such a liking to the doctor that he persuaded him, doubtless with much fine gold, to stay in England. The medical tradition was handed down from father to son for two-and-a-half centuries, but it came alas to an end with J. H. Sequeira. When he was doing his work on radiology it had not yet been appreciated how dangerous this could be and he himself told me that he was sure that he had sterilized himself.

In a country where yaws, syphilis, leprosy and many tropical skin conditions were common, a dermatologist of international repute was a godsend and Sequeira was soon working in close collaboration with the DMS.

Dr Burkitt was joined by Drs McCaldin and Gregory, both of whom, though retired, are still living in Kenya, and another newcomer was Mr A. C. King, a surgeon who had been trained under Mr James Walton at the London Hospital.

Dr Burkitt who could be described as a foundation member of the Profession in Kenya was a man of decidedly unorthodox ideas, one of which was to treat pneumonia patients by laying them on a mackintosh sheet and drenching them with cold water; some of these unfortunates actually survived this heroic therapeutic measure, but as may be imagined others did not. Burkitt held an English FRCS, but although his knowledge of surgery was encyclopaedic I would not say he was a very good operator. He belonged to the old-fashioned school which believed that to examine a patient one should see the body as a whole and those who consulted him were required to remove all their clothing; this led to an amusing, though somewhat embarrassing incident. Dr Sequeira, to whom Burkitt lent one of his consulting rooms, had picked up a European case of leprosy and he and Burkitt treated the man experimentally with injections of methylene blue and they were very hopeful when they saw that the dye was staining the man's facial nodules blue. Unfortunately the man stopped coming for his injections and the disappointed doctors were afraid that they had seen the last of him. One day Burkitt was examining an influential lady patient, as usual entirely unclothed, when his Goanese assistant tapped on the door and told him that the leprosy patient had turned up again. With a cry of delight, Burkitt thrust a bundle of clothes into the arms of his naked patient, pushed her out into the corridor which was full of waiting people and called out for the leprosy case and Dr Sequeira.

The influx of new doctors necessitated changes in the old set-up. Surgeons were now allowed to operate at the European Hospital and newly-appointed MOs were no longer allowed private practice in Nairobi. The hospital was equipped with an internal water supply and WCs were installed. A small single ward adjoining the theatre was converted into an anaesthetic room. What Harold Macmillan referred to in later years as 'the wind of change' was beginning to fan the flames of medical progress in Kenya.

In the field of education there had been a big advance; a Medical Training Depot had been established at the Native Hospital in 1929 and schoolboys, largely drawn from the Alliance High School were taught to become Hospital Assistants, Laboratory Assistants and

Assistant Pharmacists. They were all given basic instruction in English in simple anatomy, physiology and pharmacology. The Hospital Assistants had ward training in nursing and elementary medicine and the course lasted for four years. The object was to make competent nurses of them so that they could work in centres where there were no European Sisters and some of them were sent to take charge of country dispensaries. It was not intended to turn out half-baked doctors, but some of the most promising pupils were sent to the new Medical School at Makerere College in Uganda and if my memory serves me right, the first of them to qualify for the Uganda Diploma of Medicine was Mr Likimani who is now DMS Kenya. Mr Likimani became a very competent surgeon, especially in the field of orthopaedics under the tutelage of Mr Kirkaldy-Willis. He also rendered valuable service when he was sent to run the hospital at Narok among his own people, the Masai.

In 1932 Dr Gilks, the DMS retired and 'the wind of change' which might till then have been described as a gentle zephyr, became very nearly a gale. Gilks who was not more than an average administrator was a very competent clinician. On one occasion he was inspecting Kisumu hospital and was being conducted round by a somewhat pompous, self-opinionated young MO who showed him a case of splenomegaly which he declared to be of unknown etiology. At that time kala-azar had not been reported in Kenya, but Gilks, after taking a detailed history and making a careful physical examination, suggested, much to the MO's surprise, that a blood-slide, a blood-culture on NNN medium or a spleen smear, might reveal the presence of Leishman-Donovan bodies. The diagnosis of kala-azar was confirmed.

Dr Paterson who succeeded Gilks was no clinician and had never aspired to become one; his first and only love was Public Health and he was without doubt the ablest administrator ever to hold the post of DMS Kenya under the old Colonial regime. He was however a poor judge of men and was prone to be taken in by 'yes-men'. He was also prone to become obsessed by grandiose schemes and when he was engaged upon one of them, the whole work of the Department was apt to be subordinated to his predilection of the moment. I have already referred to his scheme of 'chickens for the Masai'. The origin of this was that in the Masai country, owing to the large numbers of cattle, there were hordes of flies which were instrumental in spreading ophthalmic infections, particularly gonorrhoeal conjunctivitis. Paterson thought that the fowls would feed themselves on the maggots in the cow-dung, thus controlling the fly nuisance. In theory, this was an excellent notion, for no one who has ever visited a Masai manyatta, feet deep in cattle dung could fail to see its advantages. The basic snag was that it failed to allow for the mental attitude of the Masai.

A lengthy memorandum was prepared, the Veterinary Department was consulted as to the best breed of fowls to import and the Senior Sanitary Inspector spent all his days drawing plans of chicken coops. It was decided to provide the Masai with Rhode Island Reds and the choice of this heavy breed was about as bad for a hot country as it could possibly have been. All this prodigious expenditure of money and energy came to nothing. The Masai are the aristocrats of East Africa and they considered themselves to be the equals if not the superiors of all their fellow men, including the Europeans. Their whole social structure was based on warfare and their love for cattle has always been proverbial. A Masai might deign to accompany a white man on a shooting expedition, but he would never dream of eating any of the meat if an antelope were shot. His diet was a mixture of fresh blood and milk. To these proud aloof people Paterson sent Charles Philip to use the eloquence he had displayed at the Coast. But they would have none of Paterson and his chickens and the whole project disappeared into the limbo of the Departmental Archives. Other abortive schemes were the one for irrigating the Tana River valley and that for growing rice on the shores of Lake Victoria.

When the depression of the 1930s began to make itself felt in East Africa, stringent measures of economy were introduced and Paterson took the opportunity to get rid of some of the 'dead wood' from amongst his personnel. One of the heads to fall was that of my old friend Ogden who was still the Office Superintendent. Carlyle Johnstone who was by this time on the Headquarter Staff, suggested that he was redundant, but Paterson was highly indignant.

'Yes' said Johnstone in reply to his protests. 'But what does he do?'

'Why he is the Office Superintendent of course!'

'I know that that is what he is called.' Replied Johnstone, 'but I repeat, what does he actually do? He opens the morning mail, reads all the confidential letters and then sends the office boy to distribute them. He then sits back and reads the paper; you know as well as I do that when Ogden goes on leave it is never necessary to replace him.'

Johnstone was one of the few people to whom Paterson would listen and Ogden was retired on pension.

One of the wise changes Paterson made was to stop the constant moving round of MOs which had been the rule under Gilks. He recognized the fact that it was to the benefit of the people if their doctors remained with them long enough to gain their confidence and esteem, but he went further and decided to set up a team of specialists in Nairobi. This was in time, to fulfil a long-felt want, but that time had not yet come. There was a dearth of officers with specialist qualifications and the only one available was C. Viney Braimbridge, FRCS who was made Surgical Specialist. The influence of this man on the medical life of Nairobi and the Colony in general was profound, but he suffered from the disability of isolation. Had there been an equally good medical consultant to work side by side with him, the combination would have been much more evenly balanced. As it was there was a bias towards surgery and the tendency in doubtful cases was to have a look inside to try and find a diagnosis. There was a great deal said about chronic appendicitis, a condition which conservative surgeons said did not exist, but a great many appendicectomies were performed and a lot of money was earned by the operators.

When Braimbridge took up his new appointment he was severely handicapped by the lack of a competent anaesthetist. If he was to operate at the European Hospital he had to ring up for someone, anyone, who chanced to be at liberty to come and give the anaesthetic. At the Native Hospital there were so many fatalities and near-fatalities that Hopkirk, Gerald Anderson's assistant was called in and paid to attend the operating sessions.

I became personally involved in this situation when I returned from leave in 1932. As usual I paid a duty call on the DMS and after he had inquired whether I had enjoyed my leave he asked me if I could give anaesthetics. I admitted that I could and he told me to go and see Dr Johnstone, who was now DDSS. I walked across to his office and after another enquiry about my leave, I was again asked about giving anaesthetics and I gave the same reply, whereupon I was told to report to Dr Massey, SMO i/c Native Hospital. He did not bother to ask any preliminary questions, but as soon as I admitted that I could give anaesthetics he sent me off to see Braimbridge. As soon as Cliff opened his mouth I said,

'Don't ask me. The answer is Yes I can give the odd anaesthetic, but so can dozens of other people.'

I then had the situation explained to me and from then on I gave all the anaesthetics at the hospital.

In 1928 Dan Wilson was promoted to be DMS Malaya and Dr A. D. J. B. Williams succeeded him as DDMS. For a few weeks while the MO i/c European Hospital was on local leave, I had taken over his job and Williams brought his daughter to see me because she was afflicted by threadworms. Like the lady in Holy Writ, she had 'suffered many things from many physicians' and I was consulted as a sort of final chance. I inquired as to the remedies which had been tried and when I looked up my text-book I found there was only one left which had not been used. I applied it and was successful. Williams was tremendously impressed and decided that so brilliant a young doctor must be kept in Nairobi. This seemed to suit everybody, so I remained.

A new and enlarged medical laboratory was very badly needed and work started on one in 1929. It was opened in 1930 and W. H. Kauntze who had been Senior Bacteriologist thought of this rank as being a dead end and succeeded in getting his designation changed to that of Deputy Directory of Laboratory Services, a sound strategical move because he was promoted to be DMS Uganda in 1932.

Two new nursing homes were opened one, the Eskotene, privately owned by a Mrs Wright who was also the Matron and the other the Maia Carberry which was founded by a consortium of Nairobi private practitioners. Maia Carberry was Gerald Anderson's sister; she had married an Irish peer who had repudiated his title being a great admirer of all things American; he was also very rich. Maia Carberry was an aviator and a qualified instructor; she was the first person to fly an aircraft from Mombasa to Nairobi. In 1928 she was instructing a learner-pilot when her aeroplane went into a spin and nose-dived to the ground, killing both her and her pupil. The nursing home was a memorial to her and it was opened in 1929. Both of these homes accepted baby cases so that domiciliary midwifery gradually died out.

Paterson's policy of continuity soon began to bear fruit both in Nairobi and in out-stations. Braimbridge's mounting reputation as a surgeon resulted in the Africans overcoming their fear of surgery and they came in increasing numbers for treatment. Whereas formerly there had been plenty of empty beds in the wards, it was now often necessary for patients to double up, while operating lists grew longer and longer. The same sort of thing happened in the medical wards which were now full to overflowing.

The fixed operating days were Tuesdays and Fridays; we usually began the list at 8.0 a.m. and continued operating until the late afternoon with short breaks for morning tea and lunch. We ate our lunch in Braimbridge's office and his wife and mine took it in turns to provide us with sandwiches. Those were full, happy and rewarding days and we had a most efficient theatre staff of whom I remember with particular esteem, Abdulla who was in charge and his assistants Ali and Baranabba. Ali worshipped Braimbridge and always had clean warm underclothes ready for him to put on when he had finished operating.

Before lunch Braimbridge did all the major cases, but in the afternoon we often changed places and while he gave the anaesthetics, which incidentally he did very well, I did the minor ones like ganglions of the wrist, ulcers and some fractures. On the other days, Braimbridge would usually have operations to do over at the European Hospital and I had to cope with any emergencies which might be admitted, though I never aspired to be a surgeon. Sitting at the head of the table giving anaesthetics at the rate of over a hundred a week and watching an expert at work on a wide variety of cases meant that I learned a great deal about operative techniques so that I could do a reasonable job when immediate operation was needed to save life.

In spite of its primitive character, our operation theatre was well run and the standard of surgery under Braimbridge was high, he was satisfied with nothing less than the best and his armamentarium of instruments left nothing to be desired. The staff were trained to a hair and woebetide anyone who failed to carry out the meticulous routine laid down. On one occasion Braimbridge might have been said to have been hoist with his own petard. An up-country MO had sent down a female nurse to learn theatre work and while Braimbridge was putting on his gown one morning she noticed that his sleeve had touched the end of the table. When he held out his hands for the gloves she shook her head. 'No,' she said, 'You must first change your gown. You are no longer sterile.' Braimbridge did as he was told without a murmur.

A night emergency will illustrate the sort of situation in which any MO might have found himself. Braimbridge was operating at the

European Hospital and I was called to see a man with severe head injuries. He had a compound fracture of the skull and his upper lip was split and bleeding freely. He was taken to the theatre and I first anaesthetized him and then proceeded to repair his lip. I was rather proud of the job I had done and asked Abdulla, who was assisting what he thought of it. He agreed that it was all right, but then he turned down the towels and pointed to the skull fracture.

'I hope you don't think I'm going to tackle that Abdulla.' I said.

'Mr Braimbridge says that every compound fracture of the skull must be operated on at once.' Abdulla replied as he held out a clean pair of gloves. 'You have seen it done many times and I am here to help you.'

He was quite right of course and when a surgeon is doing a skull operation the anaesthetist has a perfect view and can follow every stage of the operation, but by the same token I thought it would be much better if Abdulla did the operation with me assisting. The man's head was not a pretty sight with splinters of bone and quantities of brain matter protruding from the wound. However I cleaned up the area and carried out the technique to the best of my ability. True I made rather a large hole in the poor chap's skull, but I wanted to be sure of controlling all the intra-cerebral haemorrhage. Abdulla was completely imperturbable and handed me each instrument as it was required without my having to ask for it. I even stopped the bleeding from the edges of the skull bones with little sharpened match-sticks dipped in paraffin wax, just as I had seen Braimbridge do. When I had sewn up the wound and sent the patient back to bed, I consoled myself by remembering the dictum of one of my teachers when I was a student. 'No head injury is so slight that it can be ignored and few are so serious that the patient need be despaired of.' In the event my man made a good recovery and six months later Braimbridge filled in the big hole in his skull with a bone-graft.

On another occasion when Braimbridge was on local leave, an inexperienced young surgeon most unwisely set out to remove a large colloid goitre. This was one of our more common operations and it was another of which the anaesthetist has a good view. It was very soon apparent to me that the operator had an extremely sketchy idea of the right way to expose the thyroid gland and I asked him if he had ever done a thyroidectomy before. He admitted that he had not. One advantage of a disciplined service was that a junior officer had to obey the orders of his senior and I told the man to take over the anaesthetic while I would do the operation. His quite natural indignation at being supplanted by a mere dope artist changed to mild surprise when he saw that unlike him I knew exactly what I was doing.

The name of Cliff Braimbridge has already appeared many times in these pages and this is not to be surprised at for of all the men who contributed their quota to the medical history of Kenya, none played a more important part than did this one man. He was an enigmatic character; a mass of contradictions; of outstanding virtues conflicting with what one has reluctantly to admit were basic faults. He was possessed of quite irresistible personal charm, but at the same time he was both vain and conceited to an almost childish degree. I held him in high esteem, but he often exasperated me almost beyond endurance. I was for years his family doctor so that I can claim to have known more about his intimate personal private life than most people; his joys and his sorrows and the dark cloud which overshadowed his later years. Braimbridge was the son of a Congregational Minister; he was educated at Downing College Cambridge and St Bartholomew's Hospital. His first introduction to East Africa was during the first war when he served with the KAR before he became a doctor. His first Kenya station was at Kakamega.

Cricket was Cliff's great love; he was for years captain of the Gymkhana side and Secretary of the Kenya Kongonis C.C. He jokingly classified patients into three groups; those who played cricket, those who watched others play and those who took no interest in the game. I was in the first group because I used to turn up on Sunday afternoon and score for the matches at the Club. Paradoxically as he admitted himself he was not a good cricketer; he was much better at golf and tennis, though he used to take quite a few wickets as a slow bowler.

In all the thirty-five years during which I knew him I never knew Braimbridge to read a serious book. He was something of a Don Juan, an inveterate diner-out, an accomplished dancer and a regular attendant at the cinema. His dress was fastidious almost to the point of foppishment, his trousers pressed to a knife-edge crease and his tie knotted as if he were wearing it for the first time. Nevertheless one didn't mind all these little foibles because he was more particular in his work than he was in any other walk of life.

What about his ability as a surgeon? This was of an unusual type;

66

he was not outstanding in any one field. His greatness, for great he undoubtedly was, lay in the fact that he could perform any operation in the book and perform it adequately, from a cataract to the pinning of a femur, from a ruptured pancreas to a Wertheim's hysterectomy or the removal of an ingrowing toe-nail. I suppose few people who are in a position to form an opinion would challenge the statement that an anaesthetist has unrivalled opportunities for assessing the ability of surgeons. I gave large numbers of anaesthetics for all the surgeons and would-be surgeons in Nairobi until after the second war. Braimbridge was incomparably the best of them. He was not a very good diagnostician and he was not a slick operator, but he was safe. Whenever it was possible he used two clamps on major blood-vessels where another man would have used one and when he tied an important artery he always put on two and sometimes three. The best testimonial I can offer to his memory is that when I myself needed an abdominal operation I could pick my own surgeon and I picked Cliff Braimbridge.

Having treated the Secretary of State for the Colonies while that gentleman was on a visit to Kenya, Braimbridge was offered the most lucrative appointment in the Colonial Medical Service, that of Surgical Specialist, Hong Kong, but he declined it with thanks and he told me that he did so because he could not bear to sever his connection with Kenya cricket. Similarly there came the time when he was the obvious choice for the job of DMS, but again he declined because this time he would not give up surgery. His two great loves meant far more to him than mere filthy lucre or worldly advancement.

When the new Nairobi European Hospital was opened in 1954, Braimbridge was nearing the end of his career as an active surgeon and he became its first Superintendent. He held the position for ten years and died a few days after an operation for colonic cancer. When I had retired from the Service in 1950 to take up private practice, my parting from Cliff was the worst part of my break with the past, but when I heard of his death I was conscious of an even deeper sense of loss. I remembered all the little humourous quirks and jokes he used to toss at me over the anaesthetic screen and I remembered with pride the rare occasions when he commended my work, as well as our stupid little joint motto made up of Swahili and French. 'Hatuna Pesa Nyingi, Lakini Tunaona sana La Vie.' (We haven't got much money, but we do see life.) If I were asked who in my opinion had most certainly and justifiably earned the love and respect of the Kenyan people, I should point to Clifford Viney Braimbridge.

CHAPTER VII

Although I was giving all the anaesthetics at the Native Hospital and had charge of two medical wards there, I was also MO to the Prison Hospital and the Infectious Diseases Hospital which latter was situated on the extreme edge of the municipal area on a site which has long since been engulfed by industrial development. The hospital compound was bounded on one side by the Nairobi River on the other side of which was the game reserve and in dry weather when grazing became scarce, wildebeest, kongoni and smaller buck used to cross the river to feed, often in broad daylight. On one occasion we had a bulkier guest in the shape of a rhino which, having found plenty to eat decided to stay. The presence of this one in our midst meant that none of the patients or dressers would show their faces outside the wards and something had to be done about it. Bill Henfrey and I often used to shoot an antelope to give our patients some extra meat, but neither of us had a rifle heavy enough to tackle this pachyderm so we rang up the Game Warden who sent a man down to cope. He did not want to shoot the rhino, but hoped that he could scare it back over the river. It was unfortunate that no one had explained this to the rhino for as soon as it saw him it charged with a noise like a locomotive letting off steam and he was forced to kill it in self-defence.

On the far side of the compound looking towards the river was a little two-roomed cabin which we called the smallpox ward since it was used for cases of that disease or for the odd patient with plague. Last thing before going off duty Henfrey used to go the rounds of all the wards and one night he went down to see a man who was recovering from small-pox. He was carrying a Dietz lantern and when he turned the corner to enter the small building, he found himself face to face with a black-maned lion which was placidly devouring the carcase of a zebra, almost on the doorstep. He dropped his lamp and took to his heels.

When he got back to the office he found the staff drawn up in line waiting to be dismissed for the night. In charge of them was one Omengo, a gigantic Jaluo who was wont to boast that his father was a lion and his mother was a leopard.

Henfrey more as a joke than anything else said, 'Omengo, your father is down at the small-pox ward eating his supper. I dropped my lantern and I want you to go and fetch it for me.'

Omengo departed without a word and ten minutes later he came back with the lamp.

'My father is still there,' he said. 'I went in to see the patient; he is much better, his temperature is normal and I filled in his chart. I told him not to be afraid of my father because he has plenty of meat and would not look for any more. Here is your lamp Bwana.'

One morning while I was doing my rounds a large snake appeared from behind a tuft of grass. It reared up its head to a height of nearly two feet and threw its head back as if to strike when one of the dressers made a swipe at it with a stick. As it fell it projected a stream of fluid at him and some of it went into his right eye. He screamed with pain and covered his face with his hands while the other men despatched the snake. The man was completely incapacitated and Henfrey led him to the office where we washed out his eye with milk and gave him an injection of morphia. This snake, the black-necked or spitting cobra does not usually grow to a length of much over six feet and the one we had encountered measured five feet eight inches. The term 'spitting' is not strictly accurate because the act is carried out with the mouth wide open, the venom being squirted from the end of the poison fangs. Its aim, which is pretty accurate is always directed at its victims's eyes and it can reach its mark from anything between six and eight feet. The pain caused is instantaneous and violent, rendering the subject powerless, but the resultant con- junctivitis if properly treated clears up in a couple of days.

It was not only into the IDH compound that wild animals made their nightly incursions for it was quite common at night to find zebra feeding on the grass verge in front of the Maia Carberry and a lion which was attracted by the calves used for small-pox vaccine production, was shot in the quadrangle at the back of the new laboratory.

Those who are the unfortunate sufferers from leprosy have always inspired compassion especially in the breasts of those who went to Sunday School in their youth or listened to Bible stories at their mothers' knees when they were young and impressionable. Leprosy is popularly supposed to be very infectious, but in fact, of all the communicable diseases it is the least contagious. Leper colonies were later established in Kenya but before they were started all cases were sent to the IDH at Nairobi where they were a perennial nuisance. They were nearly all burnt-out cases with various deformities which made them look very pathetic and they not only had extra rations, they were excused all the chores which other ambulant patients were called upon to perform. In spite of these privileges they were for ever complaining and I soon got heartily sick of them.

Bill Henfrey whose bungalow was on the edge of the hospital compound near the road began to notice that on Sunday afternoon, groups of boisterous, loudly-singing and obviously intoxicated men and women, passed the house on the way back to Nairobi. He wondered whence they were getting their liquor because there was no beer-shop on that side of the town. Liquor means beer brewed in any one of a dozen ways, or Nubian gin — a pernicious raw spirit made in illicit stills. Henfrey decided to investigate and walking along the road, he found that the inebriated revellers were coming up from the rock-strewn bed of the Nairobi River; they were staggering over the boulders and roaring with laughter when one of their number fell into the shallow stream.

Bill who knew that unless he was extremely wary he would discover nothing, stalked his quarry as if he were hunting a buck and finally, after a stealthy approach he found himself looking down on the scene of operations. There was a row of forty gallon drums behind a clump of bushes and there were all the poor pathetic lepers ladling out the booze and raking in the money in payment. Nubian gin which is nothing short of rank poison was also on sale from smaller containers. Being alone without even a stick in his hand Henfrey deemed it wise not to interfere, but later when the party was over he made a thorough investigation and reported his findings to me next morning. The lepers were using their extra rations of posho, supplementing it with more purchased out of their profits, fermenting it during the week and selling the beer on Sundays. Everyone knows that selling intoxicating liquor is one of the most profitable of all businesses and those lepers must have been very rich. Henfrey and I went down to the river and found eleven drums, the best part of 450 gallons of beer in the early stages of fermentation and we up-ended them into the river, but we never did find the still they were using to make the Nubian gin.

We were not such optimists as to suppose that we had finally put an end to this racket and I could see that we were faced with the possibility of a serious scandal if the police started investigating and found where all these drunks were coming from. I pictured head-lines in the East African Standard and the Kenya Weekly,

LEPER PATIENTS SET UP ILLEGAL BEER-SHOP.
CRIMINAL NEGLIGENCE. RISK OF SPREAD OF THIS
HIGHLY CONTAGIOUS DISEASE.

We might know that no real risk existed and that hardly any of the lepers had any residual active disease, but the public did not know these facts and we had no way of educating them. A public revelation would give the unofficial community a powerful political weapon with which to attack the Government and I sought an immediate interview with the DMS.

Paterson asked if I had a solution to offer and I said I had; I suggested building a ten-foot high unclimbable fence round the two leper wards and confining them inside it. However he would not agree to this because he said it would make the place look too much like a prison and told me to go away and think again.

Bill Henfrey and I dug out all the records of the leper patients, some of them going back over ten years and confirmed by repreated tests that nearly all of them were non-infectious. I then arranged with the Administration for them to be repatriated to their various homes. In a couple of weeks they were all back again having been notified as lepers by the local MOs, who of course knew nothing of their past histories. I repatriated them for the second time, but on this occasion I wrote explanatory letters to all the district MOs. This was successful and the problem of our beer-selling lepers was solved. The three active cases who remained and those who were subsequently admitted, did not emulate the commercial activities of their predecessors.

One duty which fell by rota to all MOs was that of acting as police surgeon for a week, but this usually meant nothing more exciting than going down to the police station and certifying the odd drunk. One morning during my spell of duty I was faced with something much more serious. I was collected by a police officer and driven out to an estate at Ruiru, some seven miles from Nairobi, where the owner of the property, a Mr Henry Tarlton had been murdered. I knew Henry quite well; he was one of three pioneer brothers and had made a large fortune by judicious dealing in real estate. By building a dam he had impounded a sizeable lake which he had stocked with fish and it was his habit in the cool of the evening to sit at his ease in a punt angling. Tarlton was a quick-tempered man who had a particular objection to any strangers being on his land. There was at that time a railway construction job being done on one side of his property and the labourers were apt to cross his land to reach the main road. On the previous day Tarlton had caught one of these men and had quite illegally given him a sound beating.

When I arrived on the scene of the crime the body had not been disturbed, but the police were in the process of taking photographs. Henry was lying face downwards in the punt with his face over the end, partially submerged in the water. When the police photographers had finished I examined the body. I found that the head had been struck three heavy blows with a sharp weapon, two in front above the brows and the other from behind. The top of the head was nearly severed and any one of three blows would have caused instantaneous death. Having heard about the previous day's incident the police went and searched the huts of the railway labourers. Under the mattress on the bed of one of them they found a blood-stained *simi*. (African sword). The owner of the room said it must have been planted in his room and he had never seen it before. What he did not know was that two little boys, children of the Tarltons' servant were playing nearby and saw him commit the murder.

At the trial, which I attended as a witness the two small boys were also called as witnesses. One would have been about eight years old and his brother perhaps a year younger. If they had gone into the witness-box they were so short that they would have been invisible, so they gave their evidence standing in the well of the Court in front of the Judge's bench. Hand-in-hand they stood together and their shrill voices could be heard in every corner of the room. They, the policeman who had made the arrest and I were the only witnesses for the prosecution and when our evidence had been given Counsel for the defence rose and asked for that of the two little boys to be ruled out of order because of the extreme youth of the witnesses. The Judge leaned forward and said,

'Never in my judicial career have I heard evidence more convincingly and clearly given. I believe every word of it.'

African cases were not tried by jury, but three assessors sat in

Court and gave their opinions after the case was finished. They were usually Elders chosen from the same tribe as the accused man. In this instance they all agreed that the prisoner was guilty. The Judge pronounced sentence of death and in due time the man was executed.

There was a period when staff was so short that at one and the same time I had to take over the the Mathari Mental Hospital when the MO i/c, Dr H. L. Gordon unexpectedly retired on account of ill-health. Gordon must have been nearly 70 years old at the time, but he had had some psychiatric experience and Paterson had taken him on because there was literally no one else available. Mathari was a full-time job in itself, but the nature of the work was such that the European Superintendent could do all that was really essential, which was just as well because I only had time to exercise the minimum of supervision. Paterson bombarded the Colonial Office with requests for a psychiatrist and if I had been in a position to do so I should gladly have seconded his efforts, for I thoroughly disliked working there. Finally after six months a new man was sent out. He was certainly entitled to be called a consultant in his field and there was nothing whatever wrong with his professional capabilities. Nevertheless he was about as unsuitable a candidate as could have been chosen. He was a self-confessed homosexual, though not a practising one, he had been a patient in a mental hospital after an attempt at suicide and he had also been a voluntary patient in an institution for the rehabilitation of alcoholics. I propose for obvious reasons to give him the name of Smith. I was detailed to meet him and he arrived accompanied by a magnificent Great Dane dog called Obe, which he told me was short for Oh! Be Joyful.

I could fill an entire chapter with amusing reminiscences about my friend Smith, but suffice it to say that from the start he lived up to his reputation as an alcoholic and there were repeated complaints made about him. Paterson, with a naivety which surprised me at the time, sent for me and told me to make a friend of the man whose sole trouble was that he was lonely. I did my best and took him out to dinner with the result that he made me as nearly drunk as I have been so that I had to have my car towed out of a mud-hole by the dispensary ambulance before I could get home. Lonely he may have been, but eccentric he certainly was. He acquired a couple of lion cubs and began collecting chameleons which he kept in an enclosure with a fish-head stuck on a bush to attract flies for them to eat. He

74

said he wanted to study their mating habits. I don't know what success he had, but it was certainly Christmas all the time for those chameleons! Smith came of a good family and he told me that he was a personal friend of the Prince of Wales, later King Edward VIII, a statement which I had no reason to doubt for Smith never struck me as being either a liar or a braggart. He very soon found drinking companions more to his taste than I was and spent his time patronising the less reputable hotels and bars, always accompanied by Obe regardless of whether or no dogs were allowed, but Obe was so well-behaved and Smith was such a profitable customer that no one seemed to mind. He then took to turning up at Mathari late at night and bringing his companions to show them the more interesting inmates. Complaints were still being made, but when this last misdemeanour was officially reported it was necessary to take action. It was plainly futile to remonstrate with the man and when he had started on a dinking bout, he became totally irresponsible.

A Medical Board was convened of which I was Chairman and we recommended that Smith sould be retired on grounds of ill-health. I was instructed to keep an eye on him until he left for the Coast and this was just as well because he twice tried to kill himself. On the second occasion I told him that he was both selfish and inconsiderate and when he asked me what I meant I told him that since he was about to embark on a sea voyage he could save everyone a lot of trouble by writing a suicide note and then jumping over the side on a dark night. He told me I was utterly heartless and burst into tears, but my alleged heartlessness at least stopped him from any more suicidal attempts. I saw him off on the train where he was joined by a friend who was to inherit Obe. The only baggage they had in the compartment was an attaché case containing three bottles of whisky and one of gin. It was all gone when they arrived at Mombasa and Smith had to be carried onto the ship on a stretcher. On his return to England he was appointed to a mental hospital in the west of England, but he was soon sacked and went to sea as a ship's surgeon. When the ship arrived at Cape Town Smith booked a room in an hotel and killed himself with an overdose of sleeping pills. It is often said that if a person threatens to commit suicide the threat is seldom carried out. Smith to my knowledge made no less than three attempts and was successful with the fourth.

Once again Mathari was without a doctor, but this time a much more satisfactory solution was found with the appointment of Dr J.

C. D. Carothers. Carothers was happily settled at Kisii where he hoped to remain until he went on leave and he was by no means pleased when he was posted to Mathari. However, although he did not know it then Carothers had found his real métier for he had a flair for psychiatry and became very good at it. Later he obtained a Diploma in Psychological Medicine and was eventually gazetted one of the Colony's Specialists. After his retirement in 1950, Carothers was appointed to St James's Hospital Portsmouth and in 1953 he wrote a WHO monograph entitled, '*The African Mind in Health and Disease*', while in 1954 at the request of the Kenya Government he compiled a White Paper on the psychology of the Mau Mau which makes fascinating reading.

As the war clouds were gathering on the horizon, the new African Hospital in Nairobi was nearing completion and everyone was looking forward to saying goodbye to the old bug-infested buildings in the N'gong Road.

In 1938 the Kenya Regiment was formed. This was in the nature of an OTC and I was bullied by my friend Colonel A. D. Adams its OC and the OC troops for the Colony, Jackie Campbell to be its first MO. When Campbell applied to the War Office for me to be commissioned in the Territorial RAMC, the request was turned down, so I was given a Governor's commission in the Kenya Regiment with the rank of Surgeon-Lieutenant, soon after, Surgeon-Captain, a designation which I shared with only one other officer in the British Army who was commissioned in the Household Cavalry. This was why when war was declared, I was the only military doctor in Kenya.

A good deal has been said about medical progress in Nairobi, but little mention has been made of medical advances in the Colony as a whole. There were large and well-equipped hospitals at Kisumu, Mombasa, Nakuru, Fort Hall and Machakos, but the show place was Kiambu, eight miles from Nairobi and it was to this hospital that visiting Big-wigs, carefully kept away from the Native Hospital in Nairobi, were taken to be shown what the Department was doing for the African. A little piece of justifiable chicanery, but chicanery nonetheless, for the MO at Kiambu could get almost anything he asked for whereas the man at say Machakos could not get so much as a new pair of forceps without fighting for it. New hospitals had been opened in several districts, notably for the Wadigo at M'sambweni, a charming place overlooking the Indian Ocean. It was here that the

76

Coast Leper Colony was opened. Many out-stations now had two MOs so that public health work and dispensary medicine could be given much closer attention with the result that a fall in the infant mortality rate began to be noticed. Hospital Assistants were being sent to more and more out-stations and their influence on the standard of nursing in the provincial hospitals soon began to be apparent. Some of these men were very good indeed and a good deal of responsibility could be delegated to them. Had the day ever come when the dispensaries throughout the country had all been staffed with trained Hospital assistants, and the aim was for nothing less than this, the standard of rural medicine would have been as good as could be expected in a country which could never afford to provide enough doctors to cover its whole area.

In 1937 there was a half-squadron of the RAF stationed at Nairobi. They were a happy-go-lucky, light-hearted bunch of young dare-devils who were soon to prove their worth, but there were rather too many crashes on practice flights and too many irresponsible incidents to please the authorities, so Air Chief Marshall Sir Robert Brooke-Popham who was in Egypt at the time, came down to investigate. While he was in the Colony, he sustained a transverse fracture of the right humerus which Braimbridge twice reduced while I gave the anaesthetics, but each time when the arm muscles regained their tone the bones were pulled out of line. The proper treatment in such cases is what is termed, appropriately enough, an aeroplane splint which holds the arm out at right angles to the body, but urgent urgent matters made it essential for Sir Robert to fly back to Cairo and to do so with such a cumbersome affair did not seem practicable. He returned to Egypt with his fracture only partially reduced and, of course was at once given the proper treatment with a perfect result. Later in the year Sir Robert returned to the Colony as its Governor and Commander-in-Chief and it was characteristic of him that Braimbridge and I with our wives were invited to the first official dinner party which he gave at Government House.

Sir Robert had a tame dik-dik, the smallest species of antelope not much bigger than a hare and one Sunday evening this little creature ran one of its tiny needle-sharp horns into the back of his ankle. At this time I was living in a bungalow just outside Government House gates and the ADC rang up to say that His Excellency wished me to go and see him. I had gone to church and my wife had to come and fish me out of the Cathedral. When I examined the wound I found that though small, it was penetrating and I said that since it was exactly the type of injury which could result in a tetanus infection, I must give him an anti-tetanic injection. He flouted the idea, but I asked him what he thought would happen to me and my humble career if because I had neglected such an elementary precaution he, the Governor exchanged his high office for an even more exalted one in the realms above. He laughed and gave in, so I fetched the things I needed and gave him a shot of serum. He must have approved of my care for him, because two days later he sent for me and said that he wished me to act as his personal doctor. He was not always a very tractable patient and on the eve of the annual St George's Society dinner he went down with a bad attack of follicular tonsillitis. It was customary at this dinner for the Governor to deliver a quasi-political speech giving a summary of the political situation in the Colony, so his illness was most untimely. I told HE that he could not attend the dinner, far less make a speech; his temperature was well up and he was in considerable pain. It was only with the greatest difficulty that I made him see reason, but he was feeling so ill that he at last agreed to go to bed and stay there. This was on the Friday and he was a little better next morning, but when I went to see him on Sunday, he was sitting up in bed reading the *Pilgrim's Progress* to his two children. He looked very sheepish when I was shown in and told me that he always read Bunyan's book to his children on Sundays and did not like to disappoint them. I told him that a sore throat was a sore throat even if it happened to belong to a gubernatorial Air Chief Marshall and gently taking the book from his hands I read the rest of the chapter to the three of them.

Physically the Governor was a magnificent specimen of manhood and he kept himself fit by playing squash and riding. His domestic life with his charming wife who was always known as 'Lady Brookham' was ideally happy and one would have thought that he would have stood up to the anxiety of those critical days better than most people. So he did for he was eminently capable of coping with any situation and making all the important decisions which were required, but the impact on his mind gave rise to insomnia. Prior to coming to Kenya Sir Robert had been on a vitally important diplomatic mission to Egypt and though this had reached a satisfactory conclusion it was not followed by a suitable interval of leave. To a man of his acute intelligence it was obvious that war was imminent and carrying the heavy weight of responsibility which he did, his anxiety was such that he just could not sleep. He consulted me, but like so many men of his type he had a rooted objection to taking any form of soporific and nothing I could suggest seemed to help him. I tried going up in the late evening and taking him out for a walk immediately before retiring; he would go to bed and fall asleep, but then at 2.0 a.m. he would wake up and remain turning restlessly from side to side until morning.

I suggested that a complete rest on holiday might, by interrupting the routine of work, change his sleeping habits as well. I discussed this with Lady Brookham and the Private Secretary and we decided that if HE could be persuaded to go away, it must be to some place so remote that he would be out of touch with day-to-day events while still being available if a real emergency should arise. We decided that Lamu would do very well because we knew that the Governor would find much to interest him there in the old Arab town with its many ancient ruins. Everything had been satisfactorily arranged when Lady Brookham's personal secretary was taken ill and had to be sent back to England. There was no regular air service at that time and no ship was sailing for several days, so Sir Robert said that his holiday must be cancelled. He would not go away without his wife and he would not leave the girl at Government House with no responsible person to look after her. I was only concerned with the Governor's helath, so when I saw my carefully-laid plan in danger of collapse, I had the temerity to offer to stay at GH until it was time for the girl to leave and then arrange for an escort to take her to Mombasa. My offer was accepted, Sir Robert slept well at Lamu and returned much refreshed, but within a few days his insomnia was as bad as ever.

By July 1939 it was evident to me that Sir Robert was nearing the end of his tether and I feared a possible breakdown. Secret telegrams were coming in a ceaseless stream at all hours of the day and night and I used to go up to GH and help the Private Secretary with the decoding of them. I again discussed the situation with Lady Brookham and the PS and we agreed that since there could be no letting up in the pressure of work and the seriousness of the international crisis, the Governor's condition could not be expected to improve unless something could be done to help him.

Then my mind turned to England and her Prime Minister who bore an even heavier weight of responsibility and I recalled that he had a week-end retreat at Chequers where he could retire for a change of scene. If we could only find a 'Chequers' for our patient it might do the trick. Fifteen miles from Nairobi, on the slopes of the N'gong Hills was the house of the PC for the Masai district. It was a large, comfortable isolated house which I thought would be ideal for the purpose and I asked Lady Brookham if she would back me up if I tried to have it made available as a week-end retreat for HE; she agreed enthusiastically. My chances of bringing this off were by no means good. I had to start by convincing the DMS and then get him to pass me on to the Chief Secretary who was the only person who could arrange for the PC to be moved out of his comfortable home and all this had to be done without the Governor getting wind of what was going on. If he had found out I doubt if even Lady Brookham could have protected me from his wrath.

When I tackled Paterson he needed very little convincing when I put the issue squarely before him and he at once arranged for me to see the Chief Secretary whom I fortunately knew personally. Here things were much more difficult. The CS saw the force of my arguments, but a PC is not a person who can be treated lightly and the man with whom we had to deal was not going to be easy to handle. However the CS saw that something had to be done and he went ahead and made the very difficult arrangements. He told me afterwards that the PC was furious and at first insisted on his prerogative of appealing to the Governor which would have ruined the whole project. He allowed himself to be persuaded, however and Lady Brookham sent silver, linen, glass and crockery to N'gong while I was left with the most perilous part of the business, that of telling HE what we had done. I knew that he would be very angry at not having been consulted in a matter which so closely concerned him, but I also knew that if he had been consulted he would never have agreed to the inconveniencing of one of his senior administrative officers. The only chance of success was to present him with a *fait accompli*.

It was on a Thursday evening that I went up to GH and I began by asking Lady Brookham to be sure and remain within call. By this time I knew Sir Robert well enough to knock at his door when he was at work and try to persuade him to take a break, but this time I waited for him to come out, which he did after half-an-hour.

He asked me how long I had been waiting and when I told him, enquired why I had not come to find him. Then he told me to get myself a drink from a side table and mix him a whisky and soda.

As I put the glass into his hand our eyes met and I saw that he sensed something unusual in my manner; I decided not to beat about the bush, so I said,

'You have given me the responsibility of caring for your health, Sir. Is it not true to say that you are very near to breaking point?'

He turned round and placing his two arms against the mantlepiece he placed his head on them. I could see that he was striving to maintain his self-control and then he turned round and replied,

'You are quite right Carman and I don't know what to do about it. Perhaps it will not be long before the balloon goes up and then the tension will be eased.'

'Yes,' I said, 'but in the meantime you have to carry on and it would be a disaster if you were taken ill.' Then I compared his position to that of the English Prime Minister and pointed out that he had the advantage of being able to go to Chequers for the week-ends.

'Yes, but I have no such convenient week-end retreat,' he answered.

This of course gave me the opening which I needed and I told him of what had been arranged for him. As I expected, the storm of his wrath broke over my head and no doubt it was all the fiercer because of his pent-up emotions. He demanded to know how I, a mere MO, had been able to make such arrangements and why I had dared to do so without consulting him. A soft voice spoke over my shoulder and I knew that a staunch ally had come to my assistance.

'My dear Bob,' said Lady Brookham, 'you know very well that if we had told you about this plan you would have refused to let us carry on.'

'Did you say, "We"?' cried HE. 'Do you mean to tell me that you were a party to this plot?'

'Of course I was. Surely you don't suppose that Dr Carman would have acted in this way without my consent? I not only agreed to it, I told him on no account to let you know what was happening. There is nothing for you to do except to submit with a good grace to your doctor's orders. All the GH silver, linen and crockery are already at N'gong and on Saturday after lunch you will have nothing to do, but get in the car and drive to that nice house for a quiet week-end in the country.'

Whatever Sir Robert would have liked to do to me, he saw the force of his wife's arguments and agreed to fall in with the plan.

Lady Brookham had an official engagement at Kericho on that

Saturday and would have to go there escorted by the ADC. This meant that Jack Howes, the Private Secretary would be going to N'gong with HE. In the morning I was in the operating theatre at the European Hospital, when I got a message asking me to ring up Government House, which I did as soon as I was free. It was Jack Howes; he had been smitten with a bout of 'flu and was in bed with a high temperature; there was no one else to go with the Governor so the whole thing was off.

'That be damned for a tale.' I said, 'you get through to HE on your internal blower and ask him if he will have me for a temporary ADC until Monday morning.'

In a few moments he was back on the line and said that Sir Robert agreed provided I went as a friend and not as a damned interfering doctor.

So I went up to GH to lunch and in due course off with the Governor in his motor car with the little Union Jack fluttering on top of the radiator. The outcome was that everything went splendidly. We went for a long walk on the hills after tea and HE twitted me because I got out of breath while he did not. After dinner he fell asleep in his chair by the fire and when I woke him up to go to bed he told me to have him called at 7.30 a.m. I risked his displeasure by doing no such thing and he slept for ten hours straight off. Lady Brookham came back on the Sunday afternoon and she and her husband went for another long walk. We returned to Nairobi on the Monday morning and Sir Robert continued to spend his week-ends at N'gong until the war started and he was recalled for service with the RAF.

When I went up to say goodbye he was quite his normal self and full of confidence. He shook me cordially by the hand and said,

'Thank you for looking after me Carman. I did sometimes do what you told me didn't I?'

Sir Robert was one of the greatest, if not the greatest gentleman whom it has been my privilege to meet and I was very grieved when I heard of his death some years after the end of the war.

CHAPTER VIII

In 1937 and 1938, a project was conceived to build a multi-racial Group Hospital for Nairobi in juxtaposition with the new Medical Research Laboratory. There were to be separate ward-blocks for Africans, Asians and Europeans, but the administration and as many as possible of the ancillary services would be centralized. The advantages of such an arrangement are obvious. Dr T. Farnworth Anderson was sent to South Africa to consult with the Government Architect, Mr Dangerfield who had considerable experience in hospital construction; the tour of the country was arranged by Dr Orenstein. Anderson and Dangerfield drew up a tentative scheme for the group hospital with 500 African beds and smaller Asian and European blocks. Subsequently Farnworth Anderson went on leave to England and while he was there he studied hospital planning, administration and equipment.

When the war started in 1939, the African part of the hospital was nearly completed, but the plan for a group hospital had been abandoned because of political pressure. The African hospital was commandeered by the Army as soon as it was finished.

In 1940 when Italy entered the war, South Africa sent troops to Kenya and Dr Orenstein was in charge of their medical services with the rank of Brigadier. He returned to South Africa after the fall of Addis Ababa and the conquest of Abyssinia. He was honoured with the CB, CMG and the CBE.

Dr Farnworth Anderson served through the Abyssinia campaign and reached the rank of Lieutenant Colonel. In 1943 he was given a military MBE and promoted to full Colonel. When Colonel Gilkes ADMS Somaliland was killed, Farnworth Anderson succeeded him and was first made ADMS and later DMS and he was demobilized in 1946. In 1949 he was made first ADMS and then DMS of Kenya. It was during his tenure of office that Health Centres began to be established in Kenya, though this was only one of the many important improvements which he introduced. The two first health centres were at Githunguri in the Kikuyu country and at Kwale in the Digo territory. In 1953 a home and training centre for female African nurses was started near the new African hospital which had been handed back in 1949 to the civil authority and officially opened as the King George VI Hospital in 1951. Subsequently the status of the Kenya Registered Nurses was recognized by the General Nursing Council in England and was accepted as the equivalent of the SRN.

The new European Hospital was built on the old polo ground in the N'gong Road and it was opened in 1954. The Infectious diseases Hospital lay in an area which was scheduled for industrial development, indeed Dr Farnworth Anderson says in his unpublished memoirs that it narrowly escaped being bull-dozed down before it had been evacuated. It was moved up to a new site near the expanding hospital complex in 1954. Dr Farnworth Anderson retired in 1956 and was honoured by receiving the CMG.

When war was declared on 3 September 1939, although it had been expected by any intelligent person competent to weigh up the situation, it nevertheless came as a profound shock. Advances, particularly in the field of aeronautics, had been such that devastating air-raids were anticipated and of course no part of the world was immune. At first there was doubt as to what line Mussolini would take and on Kenya's northern frontier lay the Italian held territory of Abyssinia whence the whole of East Africa was wide open to attack. If the Italians had launched an attack at that time there would have been literally no means of resisting the attack: not a single tank or armoured car was available.

Within a matter of hours a reserve RAMC Officer who had retired to the peace of his native Ireland was recalled to the colours and flown out to Nairobi with a skeleton staff. Having myself been mobilized with the Kenya Regiment, I was the only doctor in uniform, so I went at once to report to this new ADMS. I cannot remember how long this gentleman remained in office, but the only definite order he ever gave me was to buy him some films with which to photograph Kilimanjaro from the air when he went to Tanganyika. The Kenya Regiment was very soon sent up to Uganda for intensive training and as I was the only qualified anaesthetist either civil or military in the country I was told to stay in Nairobi where the new army hospital to which I have already referred was set up in the empty Native Hospital. A skeleton field ambulance was formed under the command of Captain R. P. Cormack, an ex-RAMC officer. He was very efficient and knowledgeable having had experience in the 1914–1918 war and he eventually rose to the rank of Brigadier, becoming ADMS. Although technically still in the army I was continuing to carry out my ordinary duties and much to my disgust Paterson ordered me to give up wearing uniform, though in fact I doubt if he could have forced me to do so if I had declined.

When Mussolini in the mistaken impression that the war was as good as won joined Germany, Kenya became in 1940, a theatre of war. The adjacent Colony of British Somaliland was taken by the Italians, so that the whole of our northern border faced enemy-held territory. Troops were brought up from Rhodesia and South Africa and large numbers of local tribesmen were recruited to man the many new battalions of the KAR which were formed.

Devastating as it is, war brings with it some uncontestable advantages; it calls forth all that is best, bravest and most unselfish in any young man worthy of the name and since for the time being money ceases to matter, advances are made, particularly in the field of medicine which would otherwise have been indefinitely postponed. Perhaps the most obvious of these was that Flemings' discovery of the virtues of Penicillin, which had never been put to practical use, was brought to the fore and its wholesale manufacture by the fermentation process was stimulated.

East Africa was part of the Middle East Command and Kenya was to derive considerable benefit from the fact. Military surgeons and physicians of the first rank visited Kenya from the North African front and the coming of these eminent men stimulated and broadened the outlook of the local doctors, so that whereas the first war brought medical progress to a halt in the Colony, the second one enabled it to make big strides forwards.

Among these visiting Officers were such men as Heneage, later Sir Heneage Ogilvie, Ogier Ward, Naunton Morgan and Edward Cullinan, all holding the rank of brigadier. Those of them who were surgeons operated in the civil as well as in the military hospitals and nursing homes so that first class modern techniques came into use.

There was never any large influx of military casualties, but when cases needing surgery did occur I was called in by Heneage Ogilvie to give the anaesthetics and Braimbridge regularly assisted him. He and Ogilvie had been fellow-students at Bart's so we often saw Ogilvie in

85

the theatre at the Native Hospital where he did a good many operations.

As the months passed our medical stores began to be seriously depleted and they could not be replaced. Our military colleagues helped as much as they could, but of course their own needs had to take priority. It became necessary in all but a few cases to operate without surgical gloves and it was remarkable that there was no noticeable increase in the incidence of post-operative sepsis. Cotton and linen thread largely replaced catgut for sutures and again there were no obvious adverse results. Ether being highly inflammable was always carried as deck cargo on shipboard and it is not surprising that ships' captains declined to accept it under war conditions, so we were forced to resort to the use of chloroform.

It was during the war that yellow fever presented a new problem. In 1940 there was an epidemic of this disease in the Kordofan Province of the Sudan where 17,000 cases were reported with a mortality of ten per cent: then in 1941 Mahaffy found human cases in North-East Uganda. The disease was primarily one of primates and was spread by *Aedes africanus,* but if the arboreal monkeys raid the African plantations on the fringes of the forest, *Aedes simpsoni* pick up the virus and pass it on to man. Mahaffy concluded that *Aedes aegypti* was not implicated.

Mahaffy also found positive mouse-protection tests in the Kitale and Langata forests of Kenya and this was thought at first to be the easternmost point to which the virus had spread until James Liston found positive mouse-protection tests in bush-babies, *Galago crassicaudatus,* the delightful little lemurs which live high in trees and are often caught for household pets. In those examined in the Gedi forest, the positive test indicated that the jungle type of yellow fever had existed on the coast for an indeterminate period. Here the mosquito carrier was not specified.

Paterson, who feared serious implications if there were massive troop movements southwards from Abyssinia across the Tana River, sent Charles Philip to Mombasa where he and Liston carried out a yellow fever survey. Since no invasion in fact occurred, the only practical outcome of this was the setting up of anti-*Aedes* measures on Arab dhows in case they should carry infected mosquitoes across the Indian Ocean to Bombay.

In 1942 there was a fatal case of yellow fever in Kitale hospital and a second occurred in the following year. An endemiological chart of

1920 would have shown yellow fever as occurring in restricted areas of West Africa, but by 1935 the virus had already spread to Central Africa because immune bodies were found in the local monkeys, and now in 1941 there was a belt of endemicity spreading right across Africa.

When, as was obligatory, the two fatal Kitale cases were notified to the WHO, Kenya was perforce gazetted as a yellow fever area and all the complicated and costly machinery for prophylaxis had to be set up. Mosquito-proof wards had to be provided at hospitals for the isolation of cases if they occurred and all persons travelling to and from the Colony had to be given immunizing injections. The irony of the situation is that not a single further case has been notified for more than thirty years.

When peace came in 1945 many new settlers came to Kenya and among them were a number of doctors some of whom were specialists in such fields as oto-rhino-laryngology (ear-nose-and-throats), Ophthalmology, dermatology, genito-urinary, orthopaedic and general surgery and gynaecology and obstetrics.

Under the first Atlee administration, the vast ground-nut scheme was conceived and launched in Tanganyika almost regardless of cost, with the hope of producing valuable vegetable oil and optimistically incredible quantities of food for the underfed African millions. A large staff was recruited in England including several doctors. As all the world now knows, this grandiose scheme was impractical from the start and it ended in total fiasco, but Kenya benefitted because several of the doctors from the project came to practise in the Colony.

Another source of new doctors had been Nazi-dominated Europe and these men who were able at that time to obtain a registrable qualification in England after only a year's study began to arrive some time before the outbreak of war.

Thus in a single decade the whole medical scene in Kenya underwent a profound change, because there were now plenty of doctors and specialists in every branch of medicine except intra-thoracic and neuro-surgery. A private pathological laboratory was established and two new radiologists set up in practice.

It is not easy to describe the post-war medical set-up in Nairobi because it did not develop along conventional lines with private practitioners treating their patients and calling in consultants when necessary. Before the war nearly every doctor engaged in surgery, even major surgery, whether he was qualified by training to do so or not and the reason for this was not far to seek. Money. When these men found themselves faced with a group of surgeons who held higher qualifications, they were very disinclined to consult with them in case the patient decided that if an operation were required, it was better to have it done by a specialist. This is a sordid tale to tell but it is nonetheless true and it does not only apply outside England. Doctors are human like everyone else and are influenced to a greater or lesser degree by materialistic considerations.

There had always been a tendency towards group practice, but this now became more marked and each group tried to make itself self-sufficient. One of the basic ethical principles of medicine is that the patient has an inalienable right to choose his or her doctor and if need be to ask for a second opinion. With the type of practice which I have described, it all too often happened that if a patient asked for a second opinion, he or she was sent in to the next room to see one of the other partners who, if there was the question of an operation and a fat fee, could not be regarded as being altogether impartial. A man who had done dozens of appendicectomies saw no reason why he should send his patients to an abdominal surgeon and one who had performed scores of tonsillectomies was very disinclined to call in an ENT surgeon.

These facts which I have recorded were based on incidents which came to my personal notice and were well-known to all the doctors and deplored by many. Gerald Anderson who held an English FRCS and was a Master of Surgery of London, had a well-deserved reputation for ethical behaviour and he brought together a group of consultants to provide independent specialist services. The men who formed this group covered a wide field in both medicine and surgery, but they were not in partnership; they shared consulting rooms, receptionists and overhead expenses, just in the same way as consultants do in the Harley Street area of London, but they were financially independent and had no mutual obligations other than those stated. This went far to establishing higher standards of professional ethics.

So far as the Government service was concerned, things went on much as before with slow, but steady progress. The new Native Hospital now named for Jomo Kenyatta, Kenya's first President, was opened in 1951 and a Ministry of Social Security and Health was established with Sir Charles Mortimer as the first Minister. Charles

Mortimer had formerly been Commissioner for Local Government, Lands and Settlement and was knighted by HRH the Duke of Gloucester when he came out in 1952 to present Nairobi its Royal Charter as a City.

A children's hospital was started in 1947 at Muthaiga and was made possible by the generosity of Mr E. S. Grogan, a wealthy settler who had achieved fame by making an epic journey from the Cape to Cairo at the end of the last century. The hospital was named 'Gertrude's Garden' after Grogan's late wife and it was a much needed and very valuable addition to Nairobi's medical facilities.

In 1953–1954 there was an epidemic of poliomyelitis in Kenya and a special ward was set apart at the IDH for the treatment of paralytic cases of which there were several. The poliomyelitis unit was under the joint care of Dr Eric Lawes who had succeeded me as anaesthetic specialist and Dr James Harries.

There being no medical school in Kenya at this time there was no hospital having a medical staff of the kind which exists in England, but in 1957 HH The Aga Khan founded and financed a new multiracial hospital which was named after his grandfather, HH The Aga Khan Memorial Hospital. This institution was run by a properly constituted multi-racial Committee on which I was privileged to serve. This Committee allotted beds only to medical men each of whom was competent in his own field, so that there was in fact a proper 'Staff' and no one who was not on that Staff could treat patients in the hospital. A somewhat less strict system of control was brought into being at the new European Hospital.

With the coming of independence many settlers left the Colony and some doctors whose practices were correspondingly reduced also departed. Many remained however and continue to practise under the new regime.

Mention must be made of two eminent medical men who earned distinction during the closing years of British Colonial rule.

Dr P. C. C. Granham, had while working at Kisumu, discovered the exo-eryhrocytic phase of the life-cycle of *Plasmodium falciparum*, the parasite which causes sub-tertian malaria. The exo-eryhrocytic phase is that during which the parasites are not present in the red corpuscles of the blood and it explains how relapses of malaria can occur after longer or shorter periods of apparently normal health. It was worked out by Granham by experiments on monkeys and it represented one of the most important discoveries of the century. Granham retired and went to work at the London School of Tropical Medicine and Hygiene where in 1951 he became Professor of Medical Protozoology. In 1964 he achieved the distinction of being made a Fellow of the Royal Society, the blue ribbon of the English world of science. He is now Senior Research Fellow at the Imperial College of Science.

A less distinguished, but perhaps more colourful Kenya research worker was Dr Ronald Heisch who made important contributions to our knowledge in the fields of relapsing fever, tick typhus and kala azar. Heisch later joined Professor Garnham and worked with him at the London School of Tropical Medicine and Hygiene.

CHAPTER IX

It is fitting that in writing the last two chapters of this book, I should make some apology for their very personal content, but since I was unavoidably concerned I hope I may be exonerated from blame.

The first subject which I wish to discuss is the origin and growth of the East African Medical Journal.

In 1923 the Deputy PMO, Dr C. J. (Dan) Wilson produced a cyclostyled medical publication which he called 'The Monthly Journal of the Kenya Medical Service' and the first number appeared in June. In his editorial note Dr Wilson apologized for the many and obvious shortcomings of the first issue, but using an obstetric analogy he wrote,

> For a venture such as this it is certainly true to say that a good beginning is much to be desired, yet any beginning is better than none: better a premature child than a still-birth at full term. Delay is dangerous in other adventures besides human parturition and the first consideration is to bring this infant Journal into being.

He went on to say that it was to be hoped that the Journal would have a long and progressive life before it, and this hope was certainly fulfilled, for from its humble beginning the periodical developed to become the East African Medical Journal with a world-wide circulation and in 1973 completed its fiftieth year of publication.

Its aims were to present (1) Items of Departmental News, (2) Clinical Notes, (3) Facts relating to endemic and epidemic disease, (4) Reviews of Books, (5) Reviews of Current Literature, (6) Reports of local meetings of the British Medical Association, (7) A Correspondence Column, and (8) Special Articles. The last of these early issues came out in March 1924 and the venture had proved so popular that in April there appeared the first number of the Kenya

Medical Journal in the familiar red cover which earned for it the affectionate sobriquet of 'The Kenya Pink-'Un'.

Some of the articles which appeared were remarkable, not least for the humourous vein in which they were written, the following is an example.

A most astounding advertisement has come our way. The article described and pictured is called the Wonder-Worker. Resembling a drum-stick-shaped pessary, it is said to be worn in the rectum at night while you sleep in the greatest comfort and without the least danger. It is, according to this advertisement, an absolute cure for Piles, Haemorrhoids and all rectal ailments, and also for the general upbuilding of the health of man and woman.

The directions state 'Insert the Wonder-Worker . . . Instant relief with pleasing results will follow. When itching, chafing or burning sensations appear, the Wonder-Worker should be used at once as well as if there is trouble with breaking wind causing discomfort, or sleeplessness.' In the event of breaking wind we can well picture the astonishment!

Further we are assured that it will last a life-time and may be used by any number of persons alternately. After this it is not surprising to hear that it is in use by the Clergy, Nobility, Medical Profession, Army and Navy Officers, Prominent Business men and Bankers in all parts of the world.

The advertisement of this quaint instrument is printed in several different languages, of which, appropriately enough the most prominent is Chinese.

Dan Wilson did not disclose the source from which he had obtained this priceless gem of medical advertising, but it is safe to say that it caused a good deal of amusement to his readers.

Some months after I arrived in Kenya on first appointment, I was sent for to Medical Headquarters and told by the PMO to assist the Editor of the Journal by correcting the proofs. I say 'told' advisedly, because in those days, a junior Medical Officer was not asked or requested to perform a task, even if it lay right outside the scope of his normal official duties. He was simply told to get on with it and the order had to be obeyed. Thus began my first association with the Journal, an association which lasted for thirty four years. In 1927 Dan Wilson went on leave to England and Dr Gilks nominally took over the Editorship, but he was a very busy man and he left most of the work to me except for the writing of the Editorials. In 1928 I also went on home leave but Dr Sequeira arrived in 1930 and took up residence in the Colony. Dan Wilson was promoted to Malaya and as ex-Editor of the British Journal of Dermatology, Sequeira was the obvious choice to be his successor as Editor of the Journal, a responsibility which he was glad to accept. On my return from leave in 1932 I was stationed in Nairobi and once again I became Assistant Editor, but since Dr Sequeira lived at Makuyu, I did much more than just correcting the proofs. I selected and edited the papers which were submitted for publication and transacted all the business with the printers. Dr Sequeira naturally wrote the editorials and he also compiled sections under the heads of Clinical Notes and Current Literature.

When the Journal ceased to be a mere cyclostyled sheet there arose the serious problem of production costs, but this difficulty was overcome by the generosity of Mr Rudolph Mayer, Gerald Anderson's step-father and Editor as well as proprietor of the East African Standard, our daily newspaper. Mr Mayer agreed to publish the Journal at a price of one shilling a copy on the understanding that he would receive all the revenue from advertisements. This was totally inadequate to recoup him for his public-spirited generosity.

Dr Sequeira was ambitious and wanted to see the Journal expand its sphere of influence. In a short time he secured the co-operation of Tanganyika and the name of the magazine was changed to the Kenya and East African Medical Journal with a Tanganyikan Editorial Representative. In the same way Uganda and Zanzibar were brought into the fold and a further change of title was made to East African Medical Journal. Later Nyasaland was included and the list of names in the Editorial Panel made impressive reading. All attempts to secure the addition of Northern and Southern Rhodesia in the list of participants failed because the Profession in those Colonies felt that affiliation should tend to South rather than to East Africa. In later years the Rhodesian Medical Journal was founded under the able editorship of Dr Michael Gelfand.

Soon after the war started, Dr Sequeira went back to live in England and his place was taken by Dr Jex-Blake. This was another wise choice because Jex-Blake had a wide experience of medical writing and he was a very able occupant of the Editorial Chair. He did a good deal more of the work, so that my own labours were somewhat lessened. He was, however rather a martinet and treated me rather as if I were a third year medical student working under the direction of a Hospital Consultant.

It is with very great regret that I have to confess that over the years I became resentful of what I felt was an overbearing attitude. The day came when he took exception to something which I had done and treated me to a most humiliating curtain lecture. In view of the fact that I was doing all the donkey work, I decided that I could no longer tolerate his arbitary behaviour and I told him that since he found me to be such an unsatisfactory assistant, I would resign so that he could appoint someone more to his liking. I suppose he failed to find a substitute for soon afterwards he resigned the Editorship. However he bore me no ill-will, nor I him and we remained good friends.

Early on in the life of the Journal it was pointed out that there existed the possibility that sooner or later an action might be brought against it in law for one reason or another and the Editor of the day being legally responsible could find himself faced with a heavy bill for damages; to avoid this disagreeable contingency, the proprietorship of the Journal had been vested in the Kenya Branch of the British Medical Association, so it was to the Council of that body, of which as its Treasurer I was a member, that Dr Jex-Blake's resignation was tendered. I was asked if I could suggest the name of a possible new Editor and the only suitable person I could think of was Dr R. R. Scott who had retired from his appointment as DMS Tanganyika and come to live near Nairobi. The Council empowered me to approach Dr Scott and asked me in the meantime to carry on editing the Journal myself. Dr Scott felt that he did not want to undertake the task and I still think this was a misfortune. The question of the Editorship was on the agenda of another Branch Council meeting three months later and I reported my lack of success with Dr Scott. I was asked if I had any other name to bring forward and when I said I had not, one of the Council members said, 'Carman has been editing the Journal for three months and helping with it for nearly twenty years, why not give him the job and the title?' There was no one else available, so I became Editor *faute de mieux*. I felt very inadequate to follow my distinguished predecessors and was conscious of many shortcomings. It was unfortunate that the members of the Editorial Panel lived so far away so that I could not consult with them more easily; some of them were very knowledgeable and did give me constructive criticism from time to time. I took over the Editorship in 1943 and continued to hold it until I retired in 1960.

The finances of the Journal had always been a headache and we had only been able to keep going by obtaining grants from the Medical Departments of the various participating Colonies and by the kindness and help given to us by Captain Claud Anderson who had succeeded his step-father as proprietor of the EA Standard. After nearly twenty years the Standard was still not making ends meet with the advertising revenue and this did not seem to me to be right. The first thing to do was to increase the circulation because until that was done it was no use trying to get advertisiers to pay more for our space.

Overseas branches of the BMA commonly levy a local or Branch Subscription over and above that which is payable to the parent body in England. In consultation with the London Office it was agreed that the Kenya Branch should increase its local subscription by an amount less than the annual subscription to the Journal and that all members should then receive it gratis. This arrangement could not be imposed on members, but the proposal was circulated to all of them and then a special general meeting was held to decide the issue. The Branch Council's recommendation was accepted with a large majority and shortly afterwards the Tanganyika Branch of the BMA followed suit. This gave us a larger, ensured circulation of getting on towards a thousand copies. At the same time I handed over the advertising side of the Journal to the EA Standard. They had recently appointed a new advertising manager and he felt that with our increased circulation he could double our rates straight away: he told me I ought to have done so long ago, but now that we could state that the Journal went to every doctor in Kenya and Tanganyika we were in an even stronger position. I believe that from this time onwards the Standard at last began to make a profit from the Journal and I can only say I hope it was a thumping big one!

There was a strong feeling amongst the members of the Faculty of Medicine at Makerere College that the Journal should be published from Uganda which since it now had its own University was the academic centre of East Africa. There were many cogent arguments in favour of the Uganda point of view and if I had felt that it was in the Journal's best interests and if the decision had rested with me, which it did not I would have been perfectly willing for Makerere to take it over. There were, however, two insuperable objections the first of which was that the Kenya BMA owned the Journal and all the members having a sentimental feeling for the old Kenya Pink-'Un, nothing would have made them give it up. The other objection was that there was no printer in Uganda who could produce the Journal to a standard even approaching that which we were used to: this was remarkable for a small country and more than once I was congratulated on the format and general presentation by English fellow editors who considered that we were indeed fortunate in securing the service of such excellent printers.

The matter was repeatedly raised by the Uganda member of the Editorial Panel, who was himself one of the most ardent protagonists of the proposed transfer, so I laid it before our BMA Branch Council who deputed me to go up to Kampala and thrash the matter out on the spot.

At the meeting which followed it was at once apparent that the senior members of the Medical Faculty were unanimous in their determination to get the transfer put through, but they were blind to practical matters and none of them had the faintest notion of the business side of production and none of them had any editorial experience. The first suggestion they made which was so absurd as to be almost laughable, was that the Journal should be printed in England and sent out in bulk for distribution locally. They had not thought of the problem of proof correction and I told them that someone had to correct two sets of proofs, galleys and page-proofs for every issue. Neither had they the faintest idea of what printing costs in England were likely to be. I was able to tell them because I had made it my business to find out how home costs compared with those in Kenya and they were in fact nearly twice as high. The second suggestion was so incredible that it nearly made me gasp with astonishment. It was that there should be an editor in Kampala who would select all the papers for publication. I should be given the title of Assistant Editor and the matter would be sent to me. I should then arrange the lay-out, do all the business with the printers, correct the proofs and produce the Journal. Of course I knew what lay behind all this. These Makerere people did a good deal of original research and wrote papers about it. The best of these were sent to specialist journals but they had no outlet for their second-rate stuff. The policy of the EAMJ had always been to encourage local men to publish their original observations and interesting cases in their own own Journal. Of course we did not print anything of downright poor quality and it

96

was sometimes necessary to re-write articles almost entirely, a task which I did myself. I thought, and still think that this was the right policy in a young and developing community which had a dual purpose in that it served, not only the readers, but the writers as well. Admittedly the Uganda people wanted to raise the scientific standard of the Journal, but this could only have been done by almost excluding the work of our less experienced writers and so reversing our whole policy. The international reputation which the Journal had earned for itself was ample evidence of the fact that its scientific standards were at least adequate and this was shown by the fact that our papers were more and more frequently found in the bibliographies of foreign journals.

I told the consultants that if they were so keen to raise our scientific standards they should publish some of the work which they sent to specialist periodicals in our pages and with my tongue in my cheek I went on to say that if they were public-spirited enough to do this then the reading public would be forced to buy the EAMJ in order to keep abreast with current research and our circulation would be doubled in six months. My final contribution to the discussion was that Makerere should publish its own journal and the meeting ended. I was as I well knew in an unassailable position because possession is nine points of the law and since the Kenya Branch of the BMA owned the EAMJ lock stock and barrel, there was nothing anyone in Uganda could do about it.

When I reported back to the Branch Council they convened a general meeting to discuss the subject and it was a heart-warming experience to hear member after member say that the Journal had always been their 'baby' and now that it had grown up, nothing would induce them to part with it. So the Journal stayed in Nairobi, or rather in Kenya, and there it still is a quarter of a century after the old controversy died of inertia.

During the years of my Editorship, I never had an assistant though as I have said I often received helpful and constructive criticism from members of the Editorial Panel. I did, however have the invaluable help of my secretary Mrs Barbara Duthie to whom by reason of its stable finances the Journal was able to pay a small honorarium. When I retired in 1960 and was preparing to leave Kenya for good, I asked my friend Dr G. L. Timms to take over from me. He agreed to do so but made one proviso.

'I will do it,' he said, 'on one condition and that is that Mrs Duthie continues to act as the Journal's secretary.'

She did so and remained at her post until her recent sad death.

There have been several Editors since Geoffrey Timms and if I were asked my opinion as to the most satisfactory outcome of the work of his various predecessors, I would say that it was the fact that recent Editors have been Africans. If my old friend Dan Wilson could speak from beyond the grave I am quite sure that he would say that there could have been no finer destiny for the Journal which he started so long ago, than that after more than half a century it should be in the hands of the African people.

CHAPTER X

The penultimate chapter of this book having been devoted to the history and growth of the East African Journal, this, its last is concerned with the evolution of surgery in Kenya in relation to the science and art of anaesthesia. It is not always recognized that without the great improvement in anaesthetic methods and techniques which have taken place during the past thirty years, many of the more sophisticated modern branches of surgery could never have come into being.

It was in 1847 that anaesthetics were first used and at first by no means all surgeons were in favour of the new method. Those who were, regarded the administrators of the narcotics as very inferior members of the Profession and this attitude persisted for many years. Anaesthetists were looked upon as sort of 'plumbers' mates' and even those on the staffs of the great teaching hospitals used them as scapegoats and shouted at them when things did not go well with an operation. Men and women who qualified fifty years ago will remember the undignified and bullying behaviour of a certain type of surgeon which was all too common, and these 'Lords of the Theatre' vented their ire indescriminately on anaesthetist and theatre sister alike. The anaesthetist came in for more than his fair share of abuse, and abuse is not too strong a word to use. I have heard surgeons during operations use language which would have done credit to a Thames bargee. Such men were quite oblivious to the fact that without the help of the despised anaesthetist, most of their operations could not have been performed at all.

Those were the days of the 'rag-and-bottle' and I was taught to induce with ACE mixture (alcohol, chloroform and ether) and to maintain with open ether. There was no such thing as an anaesthetic machine or an endotracheal tube and if for some reason it was necessary to give pure chloroform, the particulars had to be entered up in a book which was kept for the purpose. This was because from the earliest days of its use, deaths under chloroform were distressingly common. As early as 1888 the Nizam of Hyderabad appointed a Commission under the Presidency of a Dr Lawrie to investigate the dangers of chloroform, but opinions differed as to whether the fatalities were due to respiratory or cardiac failure. In 1893 the German Congress of Anaesthetists reported that although chloroform was known to be responsible for many deaths, the replies to a questionnaire had shown that 14,615 administrations had been given without the loss of one life.

When I began my career in Kenya I was surprised to find that the only general anaesthetic in use was open chloroform on a lint mask, except when ethyl chloride was given for the opening of an abscess. This was because of a fixed belief that it was impossible to give ether in a hot climate and much less at an altitude of 5,000 feet like that of Nairobi.

At that time there was no single full time anaesthetist in the Colonial Service, nor had anyone devoted any particular attention to the study of anaesthetics in the tropics. In Nairobi the anaesthetics were given by any MO who happened to be available, so that the men who gave them never saw the patient before or after the operation and had no say whatever in the important matter of premedication. He was, in very fact just a surgeon's mate, a necessary, but wholly subordinate piece of animated theatre furniture. As for his having any say in what anaesthetic was used, such a thing was undreamed of. Fortunately chloroform is an excellent anaesthetic which gives good muscular relaxation, but by the same token it is highly dangerous if it is not given skilfully. Under the conditions which existed, no single MO gave enough anaesthetics for him to have the opportunity to gain the skill which only comes from experience and it was only those who had had a lot of practice during their initial training who were at all proficient.

It has been estimated that in all the cases where chloroform is given there is an unavoidable minimum mortality rate of one in every 700 patients. No records had been kept of anaesthetic deaths in Kenya, but I know of my own knowledge that they were not very uncommon. Death due to overdose was, of course, inexcusable, but there was another type of case which was in an entirely different category and it was particularly tragic because it tended to occur in young robust adult males. This was the unavoidable type referred to above and it is graphically described in the older text-books. The patient would die in the early stage of induction, perhaps when only a few drops had fallen on the mask and it was due to ventricular fibrillation. (Disturbance of the heart's rhythm.) The explanation is not far to seek, a young man who has had little or no contact with doctors, is suddenly faced with the unknown terrors of a surgical operation. His apprehension is out of all proportion to the seriousness of his condition and he is much more frightened than someone who is always being ill. There results an over-stimulation of the sympathetic nervous system which causes adrenaline to be poured out into the circulation. In the presence of this enzyme the action of chloroform on the heart is greatly enhanced and fibrillation and death follow. I myself had one such case which occurred during the war when ether was in short supply. The patient was a powerful young Sikh labourer and the sequence was entirely typical. I had dropped no more than fifteen or twenty minims of chloroform on the mask when he gasped and died instantly.

Cases of mild overdose were common and surgeons often had to interrupt an operation while the patient was given artificial respiration. One would have thought that this sort of thing would have inspired them to seek for a more suitable anaesthetic, but on the contrary they persisted obstinately in the belief that chloroform and chloroform alone was the right agent for use in the tropics.

In an earlier chapter I have described how it came about that I took up the practice of anaesthesia and when he heard that this duty had been assigned to me my old friend Dr Sequeira begged me not to take up such an unworthy specialty. When I explained that I had no option in the matter and though I did not in the least want to be an anaesthetist, I was forced to obey orders, he went on his own initiative to Medical Headquarters and remonstrated with the DMS, saying that my talents (sic) were in danger of being wasted and asked him to think again. His protests had no effect, but when I went and added my own, I had the doubtful satisfaction of being told that if I made good and my progress in the art of anaesthesia justified it, I might one day be gazetted a Specialist.

In addition to general medical and administrative duties, I was now giving all the aneasthetics at the African hospital and these amounted to a total of something in the order of ninety to a hundred a week, so I was rapidly gaining experience.

Cliff Braimbridge having been already gazetted Surgical Specialist did all the operations at both hospitals. I had never lost the rooted objection to chloroform which had been ingrained in my consciousness as a student and when I had become established and knew him better, I asked him why there was this obsession in favour of such a dangerous agent. I said I wanted to experiment with the use of ether; he made the stock reply that it was impossible to give ether in a hot climate at an altitude of 5,000 feet, I pointed out that the whole principle of inhalational anaesthesia was to cause the liquid to vapourize so that the resultant gas could be drawn into the lungs. At high altitudes the boiling point of ether would be lower than at sea level and that a raised temperature would still further raise the rate of evaporation. His only answer to this was that he knew more about East African conditions than I did and he gave me a direct order that I was not to use ether when he was operating.

However, when Cliff was operating at the European Hospital, other surgeons did their own operations as well as emergencies and since they were nearly all my juniors in the service, they were not in a position to order me about. Thus I took every available opportunity to try and perfect a technique of giving open ether on an ordinary Schimmelbusch mask. I first gave ethyl chloride until the patient had lost consciousness, quickly changed the mask and poured on ether as lavishly as possible, so that its effects might be established before those of the ethyl chloride had worn off. To prevent the ether vapour from escaping, I used a thick pad of gamgee tissue next to the face and enveloped the whole in a folded towel leaving only a small hole through which to pour the ether. By this method I was able to achieve quite satisfactory levels of anaesthesia and though it was inevitable that the mask became covered with snow and ice, it was easy enough to discard it and take a fresh one. Once the stage of maintenance was reached and the amount of ether was reduced, this nuisance was less likely to cause trouble.

Ether is far less dangerous than chloroform, indeed it would be difficult for it to cause death. This is largely due to the fact that with a heavy dose of ether the respiration is arrested long before the heart's action so that if the patient is too deep it is only necessary to remove the mask for a few minutes and the breathing will start again: it is hardly ever needful to resort to artificial respiration. I would be the first to admit that in upper abdominal operations it is not always possible to obtain adequate muscular relaxation in powerful subjects, but by then the stage of induction would be over and the patient would have settled down so there was no danger in changing over to chloroform until the surgeon had finished working inside the abdomen.

When I had gained complete confidence with this method, I waited until Braimbridge was doing an orthopaedic operation which did not call for muscular relaxation; I anaesthetized the patient with ether and awaited the outcome. Braimbridge was gifted with phenomenal powers of self-control and I very seldom saw him lose his temper. He soon noticed the smell of ether and calmly turning his head for a moment told me to switch to chloroform. I looked at him and said just as quietly,

'If you insist Braimbridge, this is the last time I shall give an anaesthetic for you.'

He must have realized that I meant what I said because he said no more and left me to my own devices, so we finished the operation which was the last on the morning's list. When we went across to his office to change he told me still quite calmly that he was the surgeon, that he would dictate the anaesthetic, I was the junior officer and I had no alternative but to obey.

I in my turn told him that I had not wanted to be an anaesthetist, still did not want to be one and if what he wanted was a 'Yes-man' at the head of the table he had not found one in me. The only satisfaction I was likely to get out of the job was to make some contribution to the study of tropical anaesthesia which, as he well knew, was a virgin field. I would use ether if I wanted to and if he complained to the DMS that I was insubordinate that would be fine; I should be taken off the job and I should be delighted to kiss it good bye.

'Could you find any fault with the ether dope I gave this morning?' I asked.

'No it was quite satisfactory except that it was directly contrary to my orders.'

Having played the King of trumps, I now came out with the ace.

'Before I came back from leave and Hopkirk was doping for you, I bet he used ether,' I said.

'As a matter of fact he did,' Braimbridge admitted, 'but Hopkirk is an expert.'

'Well don't you want the man who dopes for you to be an expert?' I cried. 'If Hopkirk can use ether so can I. You could not dictate to him because he was not your junior officer and if you had done he

103

would have walked out of the theatre. Because you are the great Clifford Viney Braimbridge you are determined to make me toe the line, even if I can prove as I have done this morning that I am right. You know perfectly well that chloroform is dangerous and ether is safe, but to establish your vaunted superiority over me you won't let me use it. We have now come to the parting of the ways. If you persist in your attitude I shall do exactly what I said I would in the theatre just now. If the question goes to the DMS and he supports you as he will be bound to do, I shall resign my appointment and go into private practice. Then you can find some clot who will go on poisoning people with chloroform to your heart's content. The best other suggestion I can offer you is that I should use my discretion as to the agent I use and if I ever give you a bad anaesthetic you can haul me over the coals as much as you like.'

He agreed to this and I had won the day, but I took a lot of trouble to see that the last-mentioned eventuality never arose.

One of the most serious problems with which I was always being faced was how to maintain narcosis in operations about the head and neck without endangering the asepsis of the operative field. The commonest of these procedures was tonsillectomy when the mouth is wide open all the time. The only apparatus which was available was the Shipway's warmed ether bottle which was at best a clumsy and inefficient device. In such cases Braimbridge was very patient and I did maintain anaesthesia with chloroform. This same problem had been highlighted during the first war when plastic operations around the face and neck were common, and for years attempts had been made to give anaesthetics directly into the pharynx or trachea through indiarubber tubes. The pioneer work in this field was done in England by Gillies and Rowbotham and in America by Magill. It came to fruition in 1932 when endotracheal anaesthesia came into general use.

Working in far-off Kenya, my only knowledge of this was what I read in the medical press, but Hopkirk stimulated me into action and I discussed the matter with Braimbridge who at once saw the advantages of the method and ordered the various necessary gadgets from the Medical Storekeeper. The one vital item lacking was an anaesthetic machine and the cost of the simplest of these was so high that the DMS refused to sanction its purchase. I had never seen a laryngoscope or an endotrachael tube and when these things arrived I practised passing the tubes on corpses in the mortuary.

There remained the matter of the apparatus; we tried the Shipway, but the best that could be said for it was that it was better than nothing. I therefore designed a compact little apparatus which I had made for me by an Indian metal-worker in the bazaar named Wali Mohamed. It was decidedly Heathrobinsonian in appearance with bottles for ether and chloroform, a mercury pressure gauge, a mercury blow-off and an attachment for a carbon dioxide sparklet. The various connections were made with rubber tubing and the rebreathing bag was a football bladder. The resistance to the respiratory flow must have been fantastic. Oxygen which had to be imported from England could not be regularly used as a *vis a tergo*, so I made a compressed air reservoir out of a couple of old locomotive cylinders. In spite of its glaring faults this little machine gave yeoman service and on one occasion I used it in an operation for the resection of a lung.

In 1932 there was a most important break-through in the anaesthetic field when Kropp and Tauer of the Bayer Company introduced the ultra-quick-acting intravenous barbiturate Evipan. This was followed in 1934 by the discovery by Lundy of Pentothal at the Mayo Clinic.

These two drugs were a tremendous boon to us, not only in Nairobi, but in out-stations where often no anaesthetist was available. It meant that large numbers of minor operations could now be done without the need for a full-dress general anaesthetic; the sort of things for which gas would be used in England. In addition to the ordinary short case other longer operations could be done under the barbiturates by setting up a saline drip and injecting repeated small doses into the tube. A local anaesthetic could be given into the line of the incision and in this way very ill patients could be dealt with without the need for toxic agents like ether and chloroform. One successful case of this kind was a man who, at the end of three weeks of typhoid fever when he was very debilitated, suffered the complication of intestinal perforation. Three lesions were found and repaired and the man recovered.

In addition to giving anaesthetics it was my duty to instruct the students at the Medical Training Depot in the same subject. In many of the out-stations where they were destined to go and work the MO was single-handed and an assistant competent to give a decent anaesthetic would be of great help. In many cases the operator was forced to give spinal anaesthesia and then do the operation, a procedure which though it may have been unavoidable, was nonetheless undesirable. The Hospital Assistants were taught the ethyl chloride-ether sequence and I had them working under me for three months. Many of them became very expert, but several MOs wrote in to say that when their Hospital Assistants came they could not give chloroform, only ether which was no good: the same old story over again. Dr Paterson asked me what answer he could give in reply to these complaints and I told him that I was quite sure that my ex-students could give ether anaesthetics quite satisfactorily in any part of the Colony as indeed I could do myself. He told me to go and prove it to them so I had a nice little break going to Mombasa, Msambweni, Kisii and Keruguya where I had no difficulty in proving my point, even if I did not in every case convince the MO concerned.

I had now made it a practice to visit all my patients on the night before operation and I myself prescribed the premedication which varied from case to case instead of always being plain atropine as was the rule before. Braimbridge welcomed this and if ever I formed the opinion that a patient was unfit for operation he never questioned my judgement.

We had a very nasty case of a man who had a bone impacted in his oesophagus and Braimbridge operated through the side of the neck to remove it. He was successful, but post-operative sepsis set in and the man died. Cliff decided that it was time we had an oesophaguscope and a tracheoscope, so these were ordered with a number of gadgets for fishing things out of dark tubes. These things had not been invented when we were students and Braimbridge, after taking one look at them said,

'Here, you are used to mucking about in people's throats. You had better learn how to use them.'

I took them home and practised fishing for various objects which I dropped down large-bore rubber tubes with clips on the end of them. After that I did as I had done with the laryngoscope and practised on corpses in the mortuary. Cases when they were needed were not very common, but when they did occur the new instruments were life-saving.

The first time I used the oesophagus on a living subject, I was terrified: the patient was thick-set with hardly any neck and he was very stout. He had a chicken-bone impacted low down in his gullet and I got Cliff to come along and help me by maintaining the anaesthetic. All I saw when I looked down the tube was a grey mass, but when this had been removed, there was the bone with its two sharp ends stuck into the oesophageal wall. I managed to cut it in half and remove the pieces separately without making a hole through the wall of the oesophagus. On another occasion I removed a narrow gold dental plate from the trachea of an Indian woman, a life-saving operation if ever there was one and this I had to cut in two. The only thanks I got from the husband was a demand for payment of the dentist's bill for making a new plate! One outcome of all this was that I went up several notches in Cliff's estimtion. Here was a mere anaesthetist who not only scored at cricket matches, he even did quite tricky operations! By gad! The fellow was almost a surgeon in his own right!

In 1936 I went on home leave and for the first time was able to study modern anaesthetic techniques at first hand. I studied at my old hospital, the London, for the Diploma of Anaesthetics. When I sat it it was only the second time the examination had been held and the pass-rate was twenty-five per cent of the candidates. My examiner was the redoubtable Dr Boyle and I had been warned that he would begin the *viva* by asking me two questions, the answers to which I had been told. This forecast proved to be accurate so I got past that hurdle all right. Then I was asked what I thought of the basal narcotic Avertin. I told him quite frankly that I did not like it and never used it. This seemed to please Dr Boyle who asked me what, if anything, I used instead. I told him that I had found rectal paraldehyde very satisfactory though sometimes a little unpredictable, possibly because of slight decomposition. 'But,' he said, 'Paraldehyde is a simple and eminently stable compound.' I agreed but hazarded the suggestion that the drug might deteriorate because of the heat when it passed through the Red Sea; he retorted rather tersely that paraldehyde was manufactured in England, so I explained that I worked in East Africa. So far as I was concerned that was the end of the examination, and if it had been available I am sure he would have offered me a glass of sherry. We entered into a friendly conversation about Kenya and its problems and when the bell rang for the next candidate to come in, Boyle shook me warmly by the hand and apologized for straying so far away from the primary object of our meeting. I left the room feeling for the first time in my career that I had almost certainly passed an examination. This proved to be the case and when I got back to Nairobi with the magic letters DA after my name I knew that Braimbridge who worshipped academic qualifications would push me up another notch or two in his estimation. In his view, no man however experienced or expert he might be, could ever be regarded as a true surgeon unless he held an FRCS.

I now felt that even if the cost were high, it was time we had an anaesthetic machine. Since I was entitled to private practice, I was beginning to be in demand by the unofficial surgeons and I had brought back with me, purchased at my own expense, a portable machine for nursing home use. True I had no nitrous oxide gas, but I was able to demonstrate the virtues of the machine to Braimbridge who backed me up wholeheartedly when I pressed for the purchase of a Boyle's table together with a supply of gas. It was not only the cost of the Boyle's table which had to be considered. The gas and the special small oxygen cylinders had to be purchased as well and we needed three times the normal number. One set was in use, one was on its way home to be refilled and the third was on its way back again. Paterson, who had a progressive outlook agreed and bought two Boule's tables, one for each hospital. When they arrived, I felt that anaesthetic practice was at long last on a par with that in England though I had to use the gas sparingly.

I have mentioned the shortages which were imposed upon us by war conditions and perhaps this was an appropriate point at which to relate that many of our problems were solved by South African manufacturers. They began to make ether and export it to Kenya before the end of the war and then they started to make nitrous oxide and send it up in bulk and they also exported oxygen. A subsidiary company of the British Oxygen Company was formed and we were able to have our cylinders filled in Nairobi which saved a great deal of expense.

I was now full-time anaesthetist, working at both hospitals and Paterson ratified his promise and made me a gazetted Specialist, being the first person to hold such an appointment in the Colonial Medical Service.

In 1934 there came the big advance which made possible the rapid growth of intra-thoracic surgery which soon followed and revolutionized the whole technique of abdominal surgery.

The history of the South American arrow-poison curare from the time when Sir Walter Raleigh first described it down to the present day makes fascinating reading. Briefly, this substance causes rapid, painless death by generalized muscular paralysis, one effect of which is asphyxia, but there is no adverse action on the heart and the effects pass off fairly quickly so that the subject can be kept alive by artificial respiration. American workers investigated the properties of the drug and Gray and Haldane in England experimented with it on each other. They published their findings in the Lancet in a paper which I read and a purified product called d-tubocurarine-chloride was put on the market. I had some sent out by air-mail; it was said to be perfectly safe in pharmacological doses, but I hesitated to use it. Then one night I was called to anaesthetize a big Sikh blacksmith with an acute gall-bladder. The surgeon was young and inexperienced and I pictured a long and difficult operation culminating in a battle to close the abdomen. Then I thought of the little glass ampoules of curare in the drawer of my anaesthetic table and I took them out and read the leaflet. This said that the dose was from 10 to 30 milligrams and I thought that here if ever was a case where the maximum dose was indicated, so having given a sleep dose of pentithal, I intubated the man, connected the tube to the machine and injected 30 milligrams of curare. In a few moments all respiratory movements ceased and I switched on the CO_2 absorber before starting controlled respiration. The surgeon began his operation and I could see that he was surprised and delighted at the degree of muscular relaxation as well he might be for the muscles were as lax as wet blotting paper. He removed the gall-bladder in what for him, must have been record time and began to close the abdomen. Still there was no sign of breathing and I began to get worried, but the pulse was full and strong and the colour was perfect. Throughout the operation I had given nothing but pure oxygen and minimal gas. The muscle sheath had been sewn up and still the patient did not breathe, but when half the skin sutures had been put in he suddenly woke up and there was no longer any need to fear permanent paralysis. It took the entire theatre staff to hold him down while the last few stitches were inserted and as soon as I took off the mask he regained consciousness and began to complain of pain. That was in 1946 and it was the last time I ever gave a maximum dose of curare in one shot.

I now began to use curare more and more frequently and before very long Braimbridge would have refused to do an abdominal operation without it. Gone were the days of fixed retraction and assistants straining to keep the wound open and the operating time was greatly reduced, while ether was not needed at all. It was this ability completely to control respiration together with the use of the heart-lung machine which enabled thoracic surgeons to operate at leisure on the heart and other thoracic organs. Other relaxant drugs were synthesized very soon and of these I found Flaxedil and Scoline to be the most useful.

In August 1950 the Kenya Hospital Association was incorporated and acquired the Maia Carberry Nursing Home. The Princess Elizabeth for women was opened by the present Queen when she came to Kenya immediately before her accession to the throne and the present Nairobi Hospital which is now, of course, multi-racial was opened in March 1954.

By 1950 I had acquired a considerable private practice, and I decided that if I maintained it I could not do justice to my official duties I retired from the Service in 1951. Dr Eric Lawes who had been working with me for some months succeeded me and soon acquired an encyclopaedic knowledge of respiratory physiology and the physics, chemistry and pharmacology of anaesthetics, so that, starting where I had left off he soon became a better anaesthetist than I had ever been.

The apogee of anaesthesia in Kenya was reached when the world-famous plastic surgeon Sir Archibald McIndoe began to make regular visits to the Colony. He introduced me to the use of the hypotensive drugs hexamethonium bromide, and decamethonium iodide the exhibition of which enabled him to perform his delicate operations in a relatively bloodless field. These hypotensive drugs need to be given with extreme care, for unlike curare they are potentially dangerous, requiring the blood-pressure to be monitored throughout the operation and demanding ceaseless vigilance on the part of the anaesthetist. I did not feel really happy with them until I had been to England and studied under Hale Enderby and Tony Edridge who were Sir Archibald's anaesthetists at the Queen Victoria Hospital East Grinstead.

I cannot close this brief history on a happier note than to say that when I went to Nairobi in October 1973 to speak at the inaugural meeting of the newly-formed Society of Anaesthesologists of East Africa, I found that some of those whom I had trained as anaesthetists in the 1930s, were still working in the Kenyatta Hospital.